THE PLAY OF
Little
Soldier

BERNARD ASHLEY

Heinemann is an imprint of Pearson Education Limited,
a company incorporated in England and Wales, having
its registered office at Edinburg Gate, Harlow, Essex,
CM20 2JE. Registered company number: 872828

Heinemann is the registered trademark of
Pearson Education Limited

© 2006
Harcourt Education

Introduction by Bernard Ashley © 2006

16
10 9

British Library Cataloguing in Publication Data
is available from the British Library on request.

ISBN: 978 0 435 125 813

Editorial: Louise Curphey, Hilary Fine
Design: Phil Leafe

Typeset by Thomson
Cover design by Forepoint
Printed in China (CTPS/09)

Cover photo: Millenium

Acknowledgements

Every effort has been made to contact
copyright holders of material reproduced in
this book. Any omissions will be rectified in
subsequent printings if notice is given to
the publishers.

Contents

Introduction by Bernard Ashley   iv

Cast list   vi

Act 1   3

Act 2   46

Activities   94

Glossary   116

Teaching resources

To help deliver the questions and activities on pages 94–115,
teaching materials are available to download free from
www.heinemann.co.uk/literature

Introduction by Bernard Ashley

A few years ago I saw *Cloudstreet*, an adaptation of Tim Winton's novel, at London's National Theatre. It's a great story, but a bonus for me was the way it was told. The story ranges far and wide, so the many scenes were set on an empty stage with a backcloth and lighting projections, the cast 'doubling' the parts wearing different hats, and using basic props that served more than one purpose – a 'table' becoming a 'car' becoming a 'boat'. It worked beautifully – and how liberating that was! I had wanted my novel *Little Soldier* to be a film, but until I saw that production I hadn't thought it could be staged.

I wrote the play and sent it to some professional companies, from whom I had some nice comments about the storyline and the writing. But everyone had the same problem: the cast is too large, even with doubling. Theatres are all strapped for cash these days, and unless it's a sure-fire West End commercial prospect, a play needs to be cast on the fingers of one hand, two at the most.

However, *Little Soldier* is a story for teenagers, and where does one find plenty of teenagers? In schools and colleges. I knew the Heinemann play series, so I trimmed the play down to a reasonable performance time and submitted it.

The result is in your hands. Many people enjoy reading play-scripts, and some schools like to put on productions – so the story's publication as a play as well as a novel might find some favour somewhere. I sincerely hope that it does with you.

Little Soldier was first published as a novel by Orchard Books. For more information on Bernard Ashley please go to www.heinemann. co.uk/hotlinks and type in express code 5818P

Staging

The action of the play takes place in the streets, homes, school and river of 'Thames Reach' as well as in Africa's 'Lasai'.

The staging can be simple but needs to be inventive in an open space – perhaps using gobos (stage lights), slides, projected graffiti, shop and school signs, and a wheeled prop to serve as a bed, car or boat.

The piece is intended for ensemble playing with some principles doubling against a small chorus of doubling soldiers, gang members, school students, teachers, nurses, policemen and general public.

Cast list

Kaninda Bulumba, (13) *African of the Kibu tribe*

Laura Rose, (13) *Anglo-Seychellois*

Theo Julien, (13) *Afro-Caribbean member of the South London Thames Barrier 'Crew'*

Faustin N'gensi, (14) *African of the Yusulu tribe*

'Captain' Betty Rose, (42) *Laura's mother, officer of God's Force*

'Lieutenant' Peter Rose, (45) *Laura's father, member of God's Force*

Queen Max, (16) *South Londoner, leader of the South London Ropeyard Street 'Federation'*

Baz Rosso, (20) *Anglo-Italian South Londoner, leader of the Barrier 'Crew'*

Snuff Bowditch, (15) *South Londoner, member of the 'Federation'*

Charlie Ty, (16) *Anglo-Chinese, member of the 'Federation'*

Sergeant Matu, (38) *non-commissioned officer (NCO) in the Lasain Kibu rebel army*

Mal Julien, (32) *Theo's older brother*

Lydia Becky, (33) *Mal's partner, Afro-Caribbean*

Gifty, (10) *Kaninda's sister*

Sharon Slater, (12) *South Londoner*

Dolly Hedges, (11) *South Londoner*

Rene Hedges, (28) *Dolly's mother*

Kintu Bulumba, (40) *Kaninda's father*

Joyce Bulumba, (39) *Kaninda's mother*

Teacher Setzi, (40) *Kaninda's Lasain teacher*

Miss Mascall, (30) *Kaninda's London teacher*

Yusulu army officer, (25) *Lasain African*

Little Jackson, (8/9) *Londoner*

Head, *Headteacher of Victoria Comprehensive School*

Boatman, *in Africa, refuses to get involved with the war*

Mrs Rickard, *works at the Jesus Saves Tearooms*

Cabbies, *eating at the Jesus Saves Tearooms*

Policemen and women, nurses, school students, Kibu and Yusulu soldiers, London general public

Act One

The house lights dim, and before the curtain rises there is shouting, screaming, pistol shots and automatic fire. In the noise of a brutal attack the following dialogue is heard.

KINTU (*close*) In here! Get down! Get under the bed!

JOYCE (*close*) Not my children! Gifty! Kaninda!

KINTU (*close*) Down!

YUSULU OFFICER (*distant*) Every one! Kill Kibu! Every one! 5

A prolonged burst of shooting, more screams.

(*distant*) Death to all Kibu!

Off: blood lust shouts and whoops, shooting and screaming.

KINTU (*close*) Get down! Get under here!

KANINDA (*close*) There's no room!

YUSULU OFFICER (*now close*) Kill all Kibu animals! In here! They're in here! Kill all Kibu dogs! 10

JOYCE No! No!!

KINTU No! Not my children! Spare the children—

There is loud, close shooting.

YUSULU OFFICER Kibu filth! Down Bulundi road! The next house! Kill all Kibu rebels!

The shooting moves away.

Scene 1

In a circle of light a pile of four bodies is in the centre of the stage. They all seem dead, but after a few moments Kaninda pulls himself out from beneath his parents. He stands up, clutching a bleeding arm. He looks at the dead bodies of his mother, his father and sister Gifty.

KANINDA   (*suddenly crying*) Gifty … Yusulu! Hated   15
Yusulu!

Kaninda staggers off, out of the circle of light.

Scene 2

The Arrivals Hall at Heathrow Airport. Laura Rose and her father, Peter Rose, dressed in God's Force uniform, like the Salvation Army but scarlet and gold, are waiting with others as passengers pushing trolleys come through from Customs.

Arrivals Hall background sounds. Passengers from an African flight are coming through.

PETER ROSE   There she is!

Calling.

Captain Rose! Over here!

'Captain' Betty Rose – in God's Force uniform – comes through with Kaninda, who doesn't want to be here.

BETTY ROSE   (*seeing them*) Hallelujah!

PETER ROSE   God be praised!   20

BETTY ROSE	God be praised indeed!

Proudly.

This is Kaninda.

LAURA	(*to her mother*) And I'm Laura.
BETTY ROSE	Laura. God's little soldier.

Kisses her, but more of a blessing than an embrace.

This is Kaninda.   25

LAURA	Hi, Kaninda.

Kaninda, closed and defiant, just about nods at her.

BETTY ROSE	So, come on, boy, this is London – an' this is your new family.

*Sergeant Matu appears in a spot, dressed in full combat gear and holding a **KM17** one-handed at the **'port'** position.*

SERGEANT MATU	This is your family, boy. You got me? Kibu rebel army. Our aim – kill Yusulu! 30
KANINDA	Kill Yusulu!

The spot goes.

BETTY ROSE	Yeah, your family. So now we go home. Hallelujah! God be praised for the saving of this boy.
PETER ROSE	God be praised! 35

She leads them off, except Laura. The scene around her changes to Scene 3.

Scene 3

Laura's bedroom. Split stage. Kaninda's bedroom adjoins.

Staying where she is, Laura looks holy in her God's Force uniform. She turns to look at herself as if in a mirror, blinks her eyes like someone with new contact lenses.

LAURA   Could you see the eyelashes, Jesus?
My secret, my rebel secret!

BETTY ROSE   (*off*) Laura! It's your breakfast.

LAURA   (***sardonically***) Hallelujah!

Scene 4

Kaninda's bedroom, London.

On his own, Kaninda is exploring his room expertly, moving fast – as if this is a taught drill. He is suddenly drawn to the window by the sound of a ship's hooter.

KANINDA   (***explosively***) Ship!   40

The door opens – no knock – and Betty Rose comes in.

BETTY ROSE   Breakfast! It's your breakfast. So, Kaninda, how you like your room? Pretty com-fort-able, eh, London, England? Soft carpet, praise the good Lord.

A pause.

So now we just got to settle what you're   45
going to call us …

*The ship's hooter sounds again and Kaninda is
drawn away from her, not that she notices.*

You've got to call us something, so I'll give
you some things to choose from. Captain
Rose – of God's Army – is who I am. Aunt
Betty or **Tante** Betty is what some   50
family people call me. Or, I don't mind,
I'd like – please the Lord an' Social
Services an' the judge givin' us their
blessin' – if you picked on callin' me what
Laura does.   55

A couple of beats.

Which goes by … 'Mum'.

*Kaninda turns right away from her to
the window.*

Eh? What you think?

Sergeant Matu appears in his spot.

SERGEANT MATU   If you're taken, lie low, submissive as a
cringing dog, an' wait the chance, an' when
you can, run! Run! You got me?   60

*The spot goes and Kaninda turns back to stare at
Betty Rose.*

BETTY ROSE   Well, somethin'll come. Patience is a pain,
but it pays. Come on, breakfast!

She walks Kaninda off.

Scene 5

Federation Street.

*One half of the stage: this is the edge of the Federation Estate, post-war council housing and a poor parade of shops. A prominent **graffiti tag** would be 'F'.*

Queen Max comes in to lounge against a wall, wearing a skimpy top with her long legs stuck out of a short skirt. The ship's hooter sounds. Snuff Bowditch and Charlie Ty slouch through.

CHARLIE TY	Oi, Queen Max.
SNUFF	What you doin'?
QUEEN MAX	The Quick Crossword. What you two up to?
SNUFF	Dunno. Might go nickin'. Lift a **can o' squirt** an' tag the Federation F down the town …
CHARLIE TY	Yeah, the old F. Spray it over the Barrier Estate. Show that slick estate what gang's boss.
QUEEN MAX	Do some for me.

As Snuff and Charlie Ty slope off, Dolly Hedges crosses them on an errand.

SNUFF	Watch it! (*Exits with Charlie Ty.*)
QUEEN MAX	Oi! Dolly! (*She stops the girl with her leg.*)
DOLLY	Wha'?
QUEEN MAX	Where you goin'?
DOLLY	Shop.

65

70

75

QUEEN MAX	What gettin'?	
DOLLY	Sugar.	80
QUEEN MAX	Payin'?	
DOLLY	Nah. **Slate**.	
QUEEN MAX	Get us a Twix, then.	
DOLLY	(*very uncertain*) I'll try.	
QUEEN MAX	Try hard! I'll be here!	85
DOLLY	(*frightened*) Yeah. I'll try.	

Dolly is let go, and runs off.

Scene 6

The Thames Barrier Estate.

The other half of the stage: a modern and contrasting area of the same borough, on the river front. The tag here is 'Crew'. Across the river, beyond the riverside wall, there is a silhouette of a ship at the Tate and Lyle quayside. Mal Julien and Lydia Becky are working on a red Ford Escort: Lydia calling for tools, Mal fumbling for them. Nearby, Sharon Slater and other kids are talking, providing an audience for Theo Julien, who is sitting on the riverside wall watching the work on the car.

LYDIA	Give us a wrench.	
MAL	(*raking through tools*) What's it look like?	
LYDIA	(*getting it herself*) Like a wrench.	
THEO	Ford Escort! He was after a Rover but the guy was still sittin' in it.	90

The kids laugh and whoop.

MAL   This is my car, man, sho' 'nuff. What you
       tellin' these people?

LYDIA (*out from under the bonnet*) Correction! It's
       our car! Cut the chat both of yous an'   95
       take them number plates off. Be a bit useful.

THEO   See, she's **ringin' it**.

SHARON Ding dong!

LYDIA I'm doin' it up. Don' want a shinin' red **lim**
       an' plates all shot up with grease. I'm   100
       gonna strip that off an' give 'em a lick.

       Mal starts unscrewing the front number plates.
       Theo comes down off the wall. He gets another
       screwdriver and starts taking off the back number
       plate, which he will put with Mal's on the
       riverfront wall.

THEO   Good plastic! You wanna keep these plates,
       Lyd, an' swap the car. Be favourite.
       Slave labour this is.

LYDIA Tell **Abraham Lincoln**. If you wanna live   105
       with me an' your brother, you earn your
       water melon.

THEO   No choice!

       Lydia stares Theo out as Laura approaches, in a
       down mood. She is out of her God's Force uniform
       and in a summer outfit.

       During the next exchanges Mal and Lydia go
       off into the flats for lunch, and Sharon and the
       others drift off, talking.

       Laura! Wotcha Lor! (*He starts a fidgety*
       click to some tune in his head.)

10

| LAURA | Hi-ya! | 110 |

She looks all round and kisses Theo on the lips, just a peck.

Give us a breath of this river air! He's come!

| THEO | The Lord Jesus? Big J? |

| LAURA | No, and don't tempt it. The Lasai kid. Kaninda. |

| THEO | Ken Inda! Why, what's your prob with him? | 115 |

| LAURA | Nothing. And everything. |

| THEO | Ah! Am I s'posed to catch on to that? |

| LAURA | (*arms around Theo*) Well, he's … I don't know … different to what I thought. 'Course, it might not be him at all. Might be me. | 120 |

| THEO | Might be? Different? Got to be, Lor. You got more lump than porridge these days. |

| LAURA | Well, with Mum's God's Force, and me being a little soldier for the Lord and all that— | 125 |

| THEO | You need a rush of some sort, girl. Pos-it-ive! Some **Thorpe Park skin peeler**, you want, or I tell you, you're gonna turn sour as ol' puss's milk! |

| LAURA | Rush? Knowing you's enough rush. | 130 |

| THEO | **Suthink** out of the run o' stuff, you want. Gotta be a devil now and then, Lor! Cut yourself out of that holy skin! Be a bit sool. |

| LAURA | Sool? That your new word? | 135 |

| THEO | Grabbin'. Gettin' hold o' life. Sool. |

LAURA   You reckon?

THEO   **Chevvy**, **Cadillac, Eldorado**, they're sool.
But you're gettin' dull as Mal's Ford
Escort.   140

LAURA   A car's a car to me. And a person's a person.

Looking at the Escort.

Are these keys meant to be in the door?

THEO   Good ol' Mal! Cementhead! He'd forget his
own feet if they wasn't in his trainers.

He looks up at the flats.

C'mon, let's have a sit-in. Be a bit private …   145

*Theo lets himself into the car, followed, after a
good look around, by Laura. They kiss, longer than
before, till Laura breaks it off.*

Indianapolis Five Hundred, racing, an'
you're right down here.

*He slides down in the seat, one hand on the wheel,
'driving', growls a meaty engine noise.*

Raaaar … C'mon, get on the freeway to LA.

LAURA   I wish!

She slides down next to him.

THEO   Raaaar! Route Maribou to the **old Cayoo**!   150

LAURA   What's that mean?

THEO   Dunno. Nuthink. Sounds the stuff, though.

*He roars the car noises, mimes changing gear,
looks at Laura and puts his hand on her leg.*

LAURA   Oi!

But she doesn't move his hand. She puts her hair up onto the top of her head with both hands like a film star in a sports car.

THEO   Raaar!

Looks round at the flats.

Up a one-way street!   155

He removes his hand from her leg, and, embarrassed as Laura drops her hair and looks at him, he starts the engine for real.

LAURA   Theo!

THEO   'S' all right, no one's about, we're on the Front, it ain't a public road …

He starts to drive the car in a tight circle.

Sool, Lor! Sool!

LAURA   Theo! Where are you going?   160

The car revs.

Scene 7

Federation Street. Queen Max is making herself up in a mirror held close to her face. Dolly enters, sees Queen Max engrossed. She and Queen Max 'freeze' as …

Scene 8

… in a spotlight, the red Escort. Theo and Laura have changed places: she is driving, looking every bit the learner.

LAURA   I can't drive!

THEO   Well, I'm showin' you!

LAURA   It's a real road!

THEO   An' I'm a real instructor … Go down   165
there! Throw a right. Route Maribou to
the old Cayoo!

LAURA   It's the Ropeyard Estate. The Federation!

THEO   Good! Clear run. They can't afford no cars,
these sads. Go on, turn right, down there.

*He leans over and helps Laura on the wheel. The
spotlight fades.*

Scene 9

*Federation Street. Queen Max is still making up,
sees Dolly in her mirror. Dolly unfreezes and goes
creeping past.*

QUEEN MAX   Dolly!   170

*Dolly runs on fast and exits in a panic. We hear the
sudden sound of Mal's car engine, being revved
too hard like a learner driver. There is a squeal of
brakes and a scream from Dolly, off.*

Scene 10

*Thames Reach Hospital. The wailing becomes that
of Rene Hedges over Dolly's hospital bed (Dolly
can't be seen). Also present are a PC, Queen Max
and a nurse.*

RENE HEDGES   Dolly! My sweet Dolly! She looks so beautiful.
Wake up, babe, talk to me.

NURSE	Sssh! Sssh!
QUEEN MAX	(*to the PC*) It was definitely a red car, but I didn't see no plates. 175
PC	You didn't see any plates, or the car didn't have them?
QUEEN MAX	Didn't see 'em. No, don't put that. It didn't have no plates 'cos I look at plates. You c'n reckon people by plates. 180

Thinks.

But she said suthink …

PC	The girl?
QUEEN MAX	Dolly. She said 'white'. Yeah, that's what she said. 'White.'
PC	White? 185
QUEEN MAX	White!
PC	What do you think she meant by that, if it was a red car?
QUEEN MAX	Search me! You'll have to ask her when she wakes up. 190
RENE HEDGES	(*wails again; to the nurse*) She is gonna wake up, in't she, mate?
NURSE	She's holding her own at the moment.
RENE HEDGES	(*to Dolly, softly*) Clumsy little cow. All for my packet of sugar. 195

To the PC.

But why run out under a car?

PC	She'll tell us. And we'll find the car, Rene. Some joy rider. We'll see who's had a car nicked.

RENE HEDGES You do that.

QUEEN MAX (*a hand on the PC's shoulder*) No, do us   200
a favour, mate. Don' find it 'fore I do. Your
justice ain't half as good as mine!

Scene 11

*The Barrier Estate riverfront. A stunned Laura is
walking Kaninda to the river; the two are walking a
metre apart. The Ford Escort is there, which Laura
skirts as if it's got a bomb in it. Theo is sitting silent
on the wall.*

LAURA You want to see the river. This is the river.

*Kaninda looks out and over at the ship at Tate and
Lyle's, moored on the other side.*

KANINDA That ship …

LAURA (*absently*) Sugar. It's a sugar ship. That's   205
Tate and Lyle's over there.

KANINDA Going where, this sugar ship?

LAURA More, coming from, you mean. From … I
dunno … where sugar comes from.
What's the flag on it? Africa somewhere.   210
East Africa?

*Kaninda stares across at the ship. He walks
away from the others along the Front to get a
better look at it. He doesn't hear the following
exhanges between Lydia Becky, who comes out
of a **lock-up**, and Mal Julien, who follows her.*

LYDIA BECKY Hey! Where's them licence plates?

MAL JULIEN	(*looking under and around the car*) I don' know, do I? I put them on that wall, sho' 'nuff. 215

Attention is drawn to the wall and Theo sitting on it.

THEO	Hi, Lor.

He comes down off the wall.

LAURA	(*a false brightness*) Theo!
LYDIA	An' I s'pose them numbers just took off on their own! Went to find another car to screw theirself onto! 220

To Laura.

You ain't seen no number plates?

Laura shakes her head. Mal and Lydia go on looking around.

THEO	How you doin'? Long time no see.

Laura and Theo stand talking earnestly. In her search for the licence plates, Lydia puts her hand on the car bonnet.

LYDIA	Blimey, Mal, it's hot! This engine's hot! You been runnin' it up.
MAL	Not since I brung it, 's mornin'. 225

He feels the bonnet, too.

Someone's been in this!

LYDIA	(*reaching inside*) 'Cos you only left the stupid keys in it!

Mal and Lydia both turn on Theo.

MAL   Theo! What you know 'bout this?

THEO   Me? Nuthin', man, nuthin'. There was   230
some kids about. But I never knew you'd
left no keys in or I'd have been straight off
along Route Maribou to the old Cayoo.

Laura turns away, distressed.

I'll have a look along here.

Goes.

*Laura follows after him. Lydia goes off with Mal in
the other direction, looking for the plates. Kaninda
re-enters, backwards, still staring at the sugar ship.*

KANINDA   (*turning*) Mozambique. Mozambique, just.   235
Back to Africa.

Kaninda is alone on the stage.

Scene 12

*A clearing in the Lasain bush. Sergeant Matu
enters with other soldiers and a prisoner with
bowed head. The prisoner is brought to stand a
few metres from Kaninda, who is joined by a line
of other boys and girls.*

SERGEANT MATU   I give the order and one of you shoots the Yusulu.
Fast! You wait more than five
seconds an' you're useless to me. One
second wait and fifteen rounds is coming   240
at you, fighting, you got me? Fighting, you
got no time for a talk with your nerves.

Kaninda and the rest stare at the prisoner.

You want in the rebel Kibu army?

He walks forward and puts a white patch over the prisoner's heart.

You want to kill Yusulu? This man has raped, burned and shot Kibu people.   245

Kaninda nods. He wipes the saliva from his lips.

(*to the line of children*) Aim for the white. His poison heart.

Turning to a soldier with an automatic weapon.

Weapon!

The soldier gives it to Sergeant Matu, who puts it on the ground in front of the line of boys and girls.

I give the order and one of you shoots!

KANINDA   (*staring hate at the prisoner, suddenly shouting*) Gifty! My Gifty!   250

He runs forward and grabs up the weapon.

SERGEANT MATU   Good man!

Kaninda lifts the weapon, which he nearly drops because it is so heavy, and points it at the prisoner. Suddenly, Sergeant Matu steps up and takes it off him. There is a moment's confusion until the 'prisoner' lifts his head. He puts on the soldier's beret of a Kibu officer.

KIBU OFFICER   (*advancing to Kaninda*) Good. You eat. This boy is a Kibu soldier.

19

Scene 13

The Barrier Estate riverfront. Sunday morning,
bright. In the distance we can hear the God's Force
silver band playing. The place is empty; Mal and
Lydia's car has gone. Kaninda, who hasn't moved
from the prevlous scene, is staring out at the river
and the Mozambican ship. He gets up onto the wall
where Theo had been sitting and looks down at the
other side. Something catches his eye, presumably
caught in wild buddleia growing there. He leans
over and retrieves it. It is a car number plate from
Mal and Lydia's car, G34 MLS.

Queen Max comes in, cautiously, stops and watches
as Kaninda moves off upstage, staring at the ship
but still holding the number plate. Charlie Ty and
Snuff Bowditch enter downstage, one from each
side, striding like combat troops on an operation.

SNUFF	Nuthink in red! You sure that car's gotta be here?	255
QUEEN MAX	(*still more interested in Kaninda*) If it went down Ropeyard Road an' threw a left, it had to come here. Nowhere else to go, the traffic's all one way ...	
SNUFF	Well, can't see it. Silver, every other metallic, an' blue, brown, green an' that other colour ...	260
CHARLIE TY	Black?	
SNUFF	Yeah, an' ...	
CHARLIE TY	White?	265
SNUFF	Yeah, that one, but not red.	

CHARLIE TY	Think about it, son! You got a dodgy car, you gonna leave it out on view? They've got it in a lock-up, probably gettin' a respray.

270

QUEEN MAX	Hang about! See that black kid? What's he got there? Ain't that a number plate? Tail him; if it is, get the number off it.

CHARLIE TY	Get him an' all?

QUEEN MAX	No, not yet, get back to me! If that car's come off this estate – an' it has – there's gonna be the biggest war since Hitler. Don't you spoil that.

275

CHARLIE TY AND SNUFF	Federation!

They do a clenched fist salute. Charlie Ty exits after Kaninda. Snuff goes the other way, eyes up Baz Rosso as he enters reading a Sunday sports paper. Snuff goes, Baz Rosso sees Queen Max, which stops him in his tracks.

BAZ ROSSO	Maxine Bendix! Out for a Sunday walk. What's a Federation waste o' time doin' down the Barrier?

280

QUEEN MAX	You just might find out, Rosso. Quite soon. You and your … 'Crew'.

BAZ ROSSO	Huh! I found out all your secrets when you was givin' out at school, Bendix. Just get off my estate, if you don't want trouble.

285

QUEEN MAX	It's a free country, Rosso. As for trouble, it's brewin', son, it's brewin' …

She goes.

BAZ ROSSO	(*shouts*) Clear off! 290

He goes, too, another way. Sharon and a couple of other kids come in from the direction he took, giggling. Little Jackson is with them, dribbling a plastic water bottle.

GIRL	What's up with Baz? Someone's **lumped** him up.
SHARON	Don't take much. He's never happy if he ain't got a grudge.
LITTLE JACKSON	(*dribbling the plastic bottle*) An' it's Jackson, 295 he nutmegs Beckham, round Rooney, takes on Grudge, beats him, looks up, sees Laura Rose an' whacks it past her!

Laura comes in wearing her God's Force uniform.

LAURA	In your dreams, Jackson! You seen a black boy on his own, anyone? 300
SHARON	We got Jackson here.
LAURA	Older.
SHARON	Why, d'you fancy a change from wicked Theo?
LAURA	No!

Indicates the God's Force music that is playing.

Someone else, Kaninda. He was with the 305 Silver Bells one minute, then he wasn't.

SHARON	(*fingers in ears*) Makes sense to me. Load of old **blow**!
LAURA	He's new in London and he's lost, Sharon.
SHARON	(*knowingly*) A lot of things get lost. 310 Look, he's here, with a mate.

Kaninda enters fast, with Charlie Ty gripping his shoulder.

CHARLIE TY   Oi, I wanna word with you!

KANINDA   (*with an eel-like twist that throws off Charlie Ty's hand*) Get off, you got me?

LAURA   Kaninda! What are you doing down here? Mum's worried about you.   315

KANINDA   Your mother – not my mother.

CHARLIE TY   I said I wanna word with you!

LAURA   (*to Charlie Ty*) Get lost!

To Kaninda.

Come on!

She grabs Kaninda's hand and takes him off.

SHARON   She's got trouble, that girl.   320

Queen Max comes in.

CHARLIE TY   Max!

SHARON   An' so have we! **Small it**, Jackson!

The other kids run off, but Sharon and Little Jackson hover, low profile – although Queen Max isn't interested in them, only in Charlie Ty.

CHARLIE TY   He's only slung the plate in the river!

QUEEN MAX   Oh, lovely! So you didn't see no number?

CHARLIE TY   He done it 'fore I got close enough. But I'll   325 know him again. 'E'll tell me the number, you don' forget them things …

QUEEN MAX   He'd better! I want these Crew hit an' run punished – 'fore they go away **inside**.

23

CHARLIE TY	Yeah, punish! School, tomorrer!	330

QUEEN MAX Now keep looking for that car. Snuff wouldn't know red from a baboon's backside.

Queen Max and Charlie Ty exit.

SHARON Crew hit and run? Federation down here? We gonna have a war, Jackson?

Little Jackson kicks the plastic bottle over the wall into the river.

LITTLE JACKSON Plop! Probly! 335

Theo comes in.

SHARON Oi, Theo, Laura's just gone off with another man!

THEO She's a lost soul, Sha, like you – you little stirrer.

SHARON What else is there? 340

Sharon and Little Jackson exit. Theo sits up as Laura comes in.

THEO (*a false brightening*) Well, little Lor! What's up with you, baby, you had no shine yesterday an' you got no shine today!

LAURA So tell me what's to shine about?

THEO Knowin' me, Sis. Rodeo an' Juliet. 345

LAURA You mean Romeo.

THEO I mean Rodeo – get off my back! Lighten up!

Laura grabs Theo, almost pushes him over the wall.

| LAURA | Lighten up!? Talk sense sometime in your life, Theo Julien! Face facts once in a while, can't you? | 350 |

| THEO | Tell me what facts I got to face. I got a blur, nothing more, an' a blur's not facts. We was in the car, you was drivin', and a girl ran out an' you swerved – and the girl weren't there no more. | 355 |

LAURA   They're hard facts, man!

THEO   Nah, it was all in a **scoot**. They ain't proof you ran over the girl an' killed her.

| LAURA | We! We were in the car. I was driving, you were giving me a lesson. We were in it together. So now we go together and we tell the police what happened. We get this sorted! | 360 |

| THEO | They'd kill us! Not the police – the Ropeyard Feds, if they was on the same hard facts as you. You c'n forget police, Lor, that'd be the easy bit, **doin' time** in Feltham … | 365 |

LAURA   Theo!

She goes to hit Theo, but he fends her off.
She turns about in frustration – finally.

It doesn't matter down here. None of this 370
matters, not the police, not the Federation.
They can do what they want.

Crying.

But I want to go to heaven.

THEO   Ah! Quick change o' rap. Big J. So where's
        the rebel Laura got to? Where's the sool   375
        girl I knew?

LAURA   (*still in tears*) Back to no false eyelashes,
        Theo. (*Stares at him seriously.*) Just me like
        God made me.

THEO   (*whistles softly*) Whatever. Whatever, Lor.   380

Scene 14

*Victoria Comprehensive School, South London
– corridor.*

Katonga School, Lasai – classroom.

*Miss Mascall is leading Kaninda towards the
classroom, which is darkened on the other side of
the stage. Other students are milling about.*

MISS MASCALL   So, Kaninda, welcome to Victoria
               Comprehensive School. We're a United
               Nations here. We've got Catholics, Jews,
               Jehovah's Witnesses, Salvation Army and
               God's Force. We've got Indians and   385
               Pakistanis, and Sikhs, Hindus, Moslems,
               Somalis, Chinese, Vietnamese and some
               English. If we flew all their flags, the
               school would take off in the wind.

               They get to the classroom door.

               We celebrate the different.   390

KANINDA   We kill them.

               *Miss Mascall walks off. Kaninda goes into the
               classroom, which is his Katonga classroom in Lasai*

*with Teacher Setzi at the front, holding his cane, Big
Master. Kaninda sits at a desk.*

TEACHER SETZI   Work. Tasks. Full attention, today of all
days. We know about the mine. We know
Deep Road Nine has collapsed, all those
diamond diggers. We know about the   395
empty desks here today, and we mourn
their Kibu parents. But we are here to
carry on as duty calls, to learn, to
improve – and if any child is not here to
learn and to improve, Big Master surely is   400
going to help them through the day.

There is a kick at the door. The students' heads turn.

Now you got mathematics. I want heads
bowed to algebra.

*A Yusulu army officer comes in. He is not carrying
a gun.*

YUSULU OFFICER   (*reading from a list*) Teacher Setzi?

TEACHER SETZI   (*half expecting something*) Yes.   405

YUSULU OFFICER   Come!

TEACHER SETZI   Come where? What is this?

YUSULU OFFICER   Come!

TEACHER SETZI   (*moving to the door, speaking to the class*)
Remember Big Master! He is on that desk,
and where Big Master is, I am. Algebra! An' 410
no sounds to be heard but the scratching
of pens an' the dissolving of brackets.

*Teacher Setzi goes out, pushed out the door at the
last moment by the Yusulu officer. The children sit
very still.*

KANINDA   (*in a hiss*) Yusulu!

He is shushed by the others. We hear sounds of other teachers being taken out of their classrooms – shouting 'No!', 'My class!', 'Where are you taking me?', etc. Suddenly, off, shooting begins, and there's screaming. Kaninda and the others dive under their desks, and scream and shout as smoke billows into the room. Coughing and screaming they scrabble for the door and the window as a megaphone sounds: 'Dismiss! School is closed! School is closed!'

Kaninda stands and walks out of the Katonga classroom into the corridor of Victoria Comprehensive. Miss Mascall is standing there. She speaks to two girls going past.

MISS MASCALL   Turn your collar down, Ruby; that's not school dress ...   415

The girls go.

(*to Kaninda*) I hope our big school isn't too frightening for you. Fifteen minutes' break. You know where the lavatories are?

KANINDA   Seen.

MISS MASCALL   Good. Off you go, then. Oh, and I might   420
have some news for you later ...

Miss Mascall goes. Charlie Ty comes along the corridor and sees Kaninda.

CHARLIE TY   Oi! You!

Kaninda goes to walk on past him, but Charlie Ty grabs him by the arm.

I wanna word with you.

KANINDA   Take off my arm!

CHARLIE TY   Yeah, I'll take off your arm! Right off! An'   425
your 'ead!

He twists Kaninda's arm.

Down the Barrier, that car plate you 'ad …

KANINDA   Take off!

Passing students are mildly interested.

CHARLIE TY   What number was it, eh?

He twists again.

Eh? You lot know numbers? What was it?   430

KANINDA   Take off, you got me?

CHARLIE TY   What was it? What was any of 'em?

*Kaninda suddenly grabs Charlie Ty's wrist with
his free hand in a practised move – twisting it as if
he might screw it off, throwing his own head back
so he can't be butted. Impressed ad libs from the
students watching.*

KANINDA   Take off my arm!

CHARLIE TY   (*letting go*) Aaaagh!

*With his released hand, Kaninda lunges at Charlie
Ty's neck getting a choking grip on his windpipe
with his thumb. Theo comes along the corridor and
sees Kaninda walk Charlie Ty round in a full circle
like a trainer with a colt.*

KANINDA   Surrender, you? Surrender?   435

He pushes Charlie Ty away.

Don't touch again!

He walks away, towards Theo, knowing Charlie Ty wouldn't dare attack again, even with Kaninda's back turned. Charlie Ty exits in distress, choking.

BOY 1　He done well!

BOY 2　Yeah! Come on, we got PE.

BOY 1　So has Charlie Ty. Breathing exercise.

The boys go.

THEO　Ken! Pos-it-ive, man! You got some guts!　440

Kaninda checks his once-wounded arm and straightens his clothing.

He's one of the Federation. Bad gang! You made the wrong enemy there!

KANINDA　No. Chinese made the wrong enemy. Chinese got the wrong enemy. I know all right, wrong enemies!　445

THEO　Well, I'm a good friend, man, when you're pickin' sides. An' I know a gang that could use you, I sure do!

They walk off, Theo with an arm round Kaninda that he doesn't want.

Scene 15

God's Force Citadel. The Silver Bells are practising off. Laura, in uniform, enters with a group of kids. She is running an evening for the Junior God's Force. She is shining keen and wanting to please

God with her activity for Him. There are sounds of heavyish rain. Kaninda comes in to slouch on a chair, taking no part in the proceedings.

LAURA   So you've all got jumbled up letters leading
to the next bit of the Treasure Hunt.   450
Put them in the right order and you go
to where it says. The first team to finish
gets a Saint John's gospel, each!

The Junior God's Force start solving clues, moving about.

LITTLE JACKSON   Ain't you got a football? Be a better prize.

LAURA   Perhaps next week, Jackson.   455

LITTLE JACKSON   Not coming next week. Only here 'cos
it's raining.

LAURA   Well never mind. The Lord is pleased to
see you today. Hallelujah!

Sharon hovers in the doorway, out of the rain.

Sharon, come right in. You want to join   460
in the fun?

SHARON   (*looking round*) Fun?

LAURA   A Treasure Hunt! And prizes.

SHARON   You couldn't pay me!

A child runs past Sharon. She grabs his paper and reads it.

O-D-O-R. Door, i'n it?   465

CHILD   Cheers!

Looks at Laura.

31

Praise be!

Runs to the door to pick up the next clue.

LAURA   You want to join one of the teams, Sharon?
It's not too late.

SHARON   Which one's winning, then?   470

LAURA   I can't tell you that.

SHARON   What can you tell me? Can you tell me, like,
what was you up to Sat'day?

LAURA   There's ten clues …

SHARON   In that car.   475

The whole stage freezes, reflecting Laura's mind.

LAURA   What car?

SHARON   Thought you was s'posed to tell the truth
in these places. You was in Mal's car.
Wi' Theo.

LAURA   Oh, yeah. We sat in it.   480

SHARON   So?

LAURA   So, what?

SHARON   How far did you go?

*Pause. The room moves again, playing
the game.*

LAURA   (*relieved*) Ssssh! Sharon! Here – have a Saint
John's gospel.   485

SHARON   Get off! It's stopped raining now.

*Sharon runs out. Laura watches her go, despite
the clamouring of the winning team.*

Scene 16

*A landing leading to the Head's room at Victoria
Comprehensive School. In an unlit corner outside
the Head's door sits Faustin N'gensi, waiting.
Kaninda walks forward from his seat in the
previous scene to be met by Miss Mascall, coming
along the corridor.*

MISS MASCALL   Everything okay, Kaninda?

Kaninda shrugs.

Getting used to the routine? It must be very
different. You were our first person from
Lasai, you know that? I'm really pleased to   490
have you in my tutor group; you'll teach
me a lot.

A couple of beats.

But another Lasain boy's starting today.

Kaninda stiffens.

Like you, he's starting a new life here in
London. I told you how broad our school   495
is. And we do want to see the new
generation doing better than their fathers.

*She walks a very cautious Kaninda towards the
darkened corner.*

You two can be an example. You can
show how the sins of the fathers need not
be visited upon the sons. Because, as it   500
happens, he's Yusulu tribe, not Kibu.

The lights come up on Faustin N'gensi, who stands as Miss Mascall and Kaninda approach.

He's over here, waiting to see the Head.
And you're both here for a fresh start.
Faustin, this is Kaninda Bulumba. And
Kaninda, this is Faustin N'gensi.   505

The two boys stare at one another for just a second before Kaninda attacks. He chops at Faustin's windpipe to send him backwards over the chair behind him.

KANINDA   Kill Yusulu!

Getting to Faustin again.

Kill Yusulu!

Miss Mascall grabs at Kaninda as Faustin runs off. Prefects and others arrive to help Miss Mascall.

MISS MASCALL   Oi! Little thug! What's he done to you?

KANINDA   This boy Yusulu! Me Kibu! Kill Yusulu!

MISS MASCALL   No! He's nothing and you're nothing!   510
You're all Victoria Comprehensive while
you're here, Kaninda Bulumba.
Kibu and Yusulu! Listen, you leave your war
back in Africa! Right?

Kaninda spits at her and runs off in the direction Faustin took. The Head comes out of his room.

HEAD   Everything all right?   515

Scene 17

The Barrier Estate, riverfront. Queen Max,
Charlie Ty and Snuff Bowditch are lurking by a
graffitied wall – 'Crew'.

CHARLIE TY   Reckons he can fight! He was lucky, is all.
We get the African on 'is own and give 'im
what's comin', that's what we do.

QUEEN MAX   You sure he lives here?

CHARLIE TY   'S where 'e was the other day.   520

Looks up at the flats.

'E's too **yellow** to come out.

SNUFF   Messin' 'isself.

Looks at the graffiti and pulls out an aerosol can.

Scum!

He tags the Federation 'F' over 'Crew'.

See? Lovely! I c'n spell 'F'.

CHARLIE TY   Well, I ain't goin' without some result.   525

QUEEN MAX   Hang about!

She has seen something. Little Jackson is
dribbling another plastic bottle across the Front,
looking down at it. He sees the three too late,
and tries to turn and run.

LITTLE JACKSON   Oh, Mum!

He is cut off on all sides.

QUEEN MAX   What's your rush, Sunshine?

LITTLE JACKSON	Get out the way!

He tries to duck and weave, but Queen Max has him like a walnut in a nutcracker.

QUEEN MAX	Please!	530

But she doesn't let him go.

CHARLIE TY	You got a big brother?
LITTLE JACKSON	Get off!
CHARLIE TY	(*hitting him*) Well, in case you 'ave, you tell 'im this … an' this … an' this!
LITTLE JACKSON	Oooh! 535
SNUFF	(*kicking him*) An' this!
LITTLE JACKSON	Ow! You rotten stinkin' bullies!
CHARLIE TY	Tell 'im we want the number off that car plate—
SNUFF	Or the car plate. Or the number— 540
CHARLIE TY	An' some respect. The Federation wants respect. Right?
SNUFF	You tell 'im. Right?

Queen Max lets Little Jackson go and he falls to the ground.

QUEEN MAX	Come on! Ooooh! Good feelin'!

She leads them off. Little Jackson is groaning, pulling himself up. Baz Rosso runs to him.

BAZ ROSSO	Jackson! Saw that! Couldn't get down quick 545 enough, **poxy** lifts! You still got legs? Uh?
LITTLE JACKSON	(*trying them*) One. Two. If there's three, I got a result.

*Baz Rosso sees the 'F' tagged over 'Crew'. He
makes a gesture of hatred at it. Little Jackson
starts to go, just holding off the tears.*

BAZ ROSSO	Jackson! This your tooth?
LITTLE JACKSON	(*feeling and spitting*) Yeah. You c'n have it. 550 Stick it under your pillow.

*He walks off, but can't stop the tears any longer.
He decides to go home to his mother, and breaks
into a run – passing Theo coming along.*

THEO	Jackson! Baz! Wassup?
BAZ ROSSO	Theodore, I wanna know what's occurrin'. Uh? Maxine Bendix and a Chinese kid just give our Jackson a kickin'. 555
THEO	That'll be Charlie Ty, man.
BAZ ROSSO	He hang around wi' Maxine?
THEO	Like a bad smell.
BAZ ROSSO	(*clicks his fingers*) So you tell me what they want on the Barrier. 560
THEO	Dunno, straight up.

Thinking fast.

Could be Ken. Yeah, this African kid. Gave
Charlie Ty a right sortin' in school, showed
him up rotten. He's prime Crew, I tell you.
Real sool.   565

BAZ ROSSO	Needs to be good, then – if he's startin' the war. Uh?
THEO	The war?

37

| BAZ ROSSO | No one hurts little kids on my patch, Theodore. Not, an' gets away with it. I got a reputation … | 570 |

| THEO | You have. You're right, Baz. Dead right. | |

| BAZ ROSSO | I better see this Ken. He starts somethin', he helps the finish of it, don't he? | |

| THEO | Yeah. S'pose he does. | 575 |

| BAZ ROSSO | You fix it. | |

| THEO | Sure! I can fix any … most things, I can fix … | |

Scene 18

*Split stage: Betty Rose's kitchen/the school corridor. Kaninda is standing to attention like a soldier at a **court martial**. Betty Rose – not in uniform but in an apron covered with flour – is waving floury hands at Kaninda. Miss Mascall and some students are in the shadows.*

| BETTY ROSE | The school was adamant, Kaninda, adamant. You keep your war over the other side of the world. Adamant. May the good Lord help to drive that hatred out of your heart. Please, Jesus. But you never, never, never got to do such a thing again. An' I'm payin' for the cleanin' of the teacher's suit. | 580

585 |

Kaninda is unmoved. He turns to face the other way, to Miss Mascall.

| MISS MASCALL | I told you, Kaninda, this school's inclusive. Everyone comes. We've got people here who wouldn't be seen | |

dead with each other in the street, but they
work together here. You put the Victoria   590
School badge on and you're not wearing
saffron robes or a **skull cap**, a turban
or a **salwar kameez**, you're not sporting
the **Five Ks** or lighting any candles. There's
no rosaries, worry beads, prayer   595
mats or buddhas. There's just you. In
school we're here to learn, so if you want
to stay and benefit you're going to make
sure nothing like yesterday happens again.
Right?   600

Kaninda doesn't blink.

Kaninda, I know about Kibu and Yusulu.
King Ndahura of the fertile lands: crops
on top and diamonds beneath. Cura, the
Kibu king, the nomads whose cattle died.
Two peoples in one land. I see the news,   605
read the papers. I understand. It's my
subject.

KANINDA   It's my life!

MISS MASCALL   Was, Kaninda, was!

Miss Mascall and the students freeze.

BETTY ROSE   Now come here, I know what you need.   610

She goes to him and hugs him.

You need a nice big hug from your …
from someone like me. Because this is
your home, Kaninda Rose. You've come a
long way an' all, but the longest way is the
shortest way home. An' I'm cookin' you   615

Seychelles sailfish an' coconut curry. My
speciality. See how you like it. An' tomorrow,
I'll cook you what you want, one of your top
poshos or somethin', from back there, eh?
Anyhow, Kaninda …   620

She takes a breath and goes for it.

… your mum's gonna make a real nice
meal.

Kaninda looks at her and his eyes go to slits.

BOY 1	That's told him, Miss. I make you right, 'cos we're all one big happy family, ain't we?
MISS MASCALL	(*turning on him*) You'd better believe it. 625

Scene 19

*The Barrier Estate, riverfront. Laura runs onto the
Front clutching the newspaper. Sharon Slater is
there with a bunch of kids, who drift off as Sharon
goes to Laura.*

SHARON	Hi, Laura. Wassup with you?
LAURA	Nothing.
SHARON	Got the paper? What's that? *The Trader*? Local. I like the news about round here, it's more … real. 630
LAURA	Keeps you in touch.
SHARON	Do they tell you, how many—?
LAURA	(*sighs*) How many what?
SHARON	(*stares at Laura and takes a couple of beats*) How … many … number plates … does a car have? 635

LAURA	That's easy.
SHARON	A car has got two number plates. One plate on the front and one on the back.
LAURA	Well, that's the law, isn't it?
SHARON	Except for Mal's car, the one you was in 640 with Theo, when he didn't get nowhere. You said. That's got four.
LAURA	How interesting.
SHARON	Yeah, four. There's the ones on it when the police come round, there was one left 645 behind on that wall when Mal was cleaning it – an' I've got one.
LAURA	You've got one?
SHARON	An' I'll tell you its numbers.
LAURA	Is this a party trick, or something? 650
SHARON	The number of Mal's car is G34 MLS.
LAURA	That's clever. Good memory. So?
SHARON	They're the letters of her name: my real mum's. Her birthday when she went off – thirty-four – and her capital letters, 655 Marlene Leigh Slater. I nicked it off that wall when Mal went in for his dinner, like, to remember her. Left the other one. So at least one of those on that car now has got to be new. 660
LAURA	Well, they'd have to be, if you nicked one of their others.
SHARON	An' you an' Theo, you was in a red car with no plates. Just like the car in that paper. What do they call that? 665

LAURA	Coincidence. It's called coincidence.
SHARON	No, I looked it up. Circumstantial, they call it. Circumstantial something.

Scene 20

God's Force Citadel. Laura and Theo come in, Laura still carrying the newspaper.

LAURA	Come in the **Citadel**. It's private. No one's about.	670
THEO	I been barred from here! Your mum barred me, when I was ten!!	
LAURA	(*brandishing the newspaper*) 'HIT AND RUN. EVIL OF THE CAR WITH NO PLATES.'	
THEO	It is. Well, it's illegal.	675
LAURA	(*reading*) 'Thames Reach schoolgirl Dorothy Hedges was running an everyday errand for her mother when she was brutally hit by a car in Ropeyard Road, Thames Reach. Now she's in hospital fighting for her life. The suspect car was red and carried no licence plates – though from the one word the victim has said in her coma the driver was white.'	680

Theo pretends indifference.

	(*reading*) 'Dorothy's mother, Mrs Rene Hedges, said: "I'm well annoyed. I want this villain caught. I can't rest till—" ' Have you seen this?	685
THEO	Did see suthink.	
LAURA	She's in a coma, Theo!	690

THEO	Lor, what's to say we done it, man? I told you, we got blur, not facts.
LAURA	You heard the only word Dolly Hedges said?
THEO	Gi's a clue. 695
LAURA	She said 'white'. That means me. They say she was describing the driver.
THEO	Makes my case. White rules you out, you an' me. I'm black as Jamaican pride, an' you're sort of— 700
LAURA	I could be white to someone in a rush: I'm light, aren't I?
THEO	Be light, girl, be light as you can.
LAURA	(*slaps him round the head with the paper*) In Seychelles Creole there's no word for racism, you know that? Black, white, 705 in between, everyone's Seychelles. But round here colour's the first thing that goes on a police description. They'll get us, Theo – so what are you going to do about it? 710
THEO	Nuthink. Wait till they nail us. Which'll be hard, 'cos Mal's car's got its licence plates.
LAURA	'Course it has, now! And Sharon Slater knows all about it – and this! The newspaper. Even that kid knows enough 715 to get us caught …
THEO	Where's your mind headin', Lor?
LAURA	… So, what if we went to the police and confessed, now? Don't wait to be caught

but say we're sorry and we came as soon 720
as we found out what happened.

Looks round the Citadel.

That would make a big difference for me.

THEO   Oh, heaven! Well, I dunno about old J up
there – but it's what the Federation's gonna
do down here we got to worry about! 725
Told you before. There's gonna be a war, and
you'll be first target, an' me next if we go an'
put our hands up to **Babylon**.

LAURA   (*crying*) Right now I'd just as soon jump
in the river. I'm ready for that, Theo. 730

THEO   Neg-a-tive, you're not! That's stupid! Not
when we got plans.

LAURA   What plans? Who for?

THEO   You an' me. I been thinkin'. We beat
the Federation – we get your Ken an' his 735
soldier tricks an' all of us, and we do them
– an' when they're out the picture, sorted
– then you an' me, we go an' see **Old Bill**.

LAURA   You'll go? With me?

THEO   (*long pause*) Yeah, I'll do my time. Does 740
weigh, man.

LAURA   Really?

THEO   Is my name Theo Julien?

LAURA   It's the name you told me.

THEO   Be pos-it-ive, girl! You just do one thing 745
– you get Ken down here tomorrow night to
see Baz Rosso, an' we'll go from there.

LAURA   Is that a promise, then? A deal? I give you
Kaninda, and when you've had your war,
we go to the police? Both of us?   750

THEO   'Less I c'n think of a better way.

LAURA   Shake on it?

THEO   Kiss on it?

LAURA   I'm not into that any more.

THEO   All right, shake on it.   755

They shake.

LAURA   Here's to truth.

THEO   Nah. Here's to war!

Act Two

Scene 1

Kaninda's bedroom. Kaninda is sitting looking at an atlas, tracing across a page with a finger. At a knock, he closes the atlas, puts it under a pillow and goes to the door. Laura is there.

LAURA   Kaninda …

KANINDA   Yes?

LAURA   Just wondered. Do you want to come out? With me? Don't know what you're doing, but do you want to go for a walk?   5

Kaninda stares at her: what is this?

It's just, I don't know you, you don't know me. We're in the same house but we're not brother and sister. We're in next door rooms and we're a world apart. Thought we'd try to get to know each other, just for an hour.   10 How about down by the river, where you like to be?

KANINDA   The river?

LAURA   If you like. You like rivers …

KANINDA   The River Lasai, I fish, swim with my   15 father …

LAURA   But definitely not in this one. No swimming here!

KANINDA   An' no father …

LAURA   We've got a few ships. Did you have ships?   20

KANINDA	(*turning away*) Boats. Boats, just.
LAURA	There's that one at Tate and Lyle's – the sugar ship.
KANINDA	Sugar?

Kaninda comes out of his room, shuts his door, and they start walking into the next scene.

Scene 2

The Thames Barrier riverfront, further along than before. We can see the outline of the Thames Barrier. Continuous. Laura and Kaninda walk in from the previous scene. Baz Rosso is sitting on the seat of a swing, his legs out.

KANINDA	This sugar ship. It stays how long?	25
LAURA	About a week, a big one like that.	
KANINDA	To Mozambique.	
LAURA	Wherever.	

She looks round for Theo and sees Baz Rosso.

BAZ ROSSO	(*over at the ship*) She goes out on the Saturday night tide.	30
LAURA	Kaninda, this is Baz Rosso.	

But Kaninda goes on past Baz Rosso to the wall where he stares across at the ship.

BAZ ROSSO	It's good things I'm hearin' about you, Ken.

Theo appears from a shadow.

THEO	Only the best, man, only the best.

47

Kaninda turns round at this ambush, looks over the wall at the drop, back at the others, takes a defensive stance, clearly deciding which way he'll go if there's trouble.

BAZ ROSSO Theo tells me, like, you're some **mondo fighter**. Uh? You got a tongue, have you? 35

Slowly, defiantly, Kaninda shows his tongue to them all.

Same colour as mine.

THEO Ken, this guy can help you. He's the main man. What you want? Mobiles, ipods – he can get all that, can't you, Baz?

LAURA Theo! 40

KANINDA Or N'gensi? Yusulu boy, can you get me?

BAZ ROSSO N'gensi? Who the hell's that?

THEO African kid. Protected in school like he's some prince.

KANINDA (*to Theo*) You get me. 45

THEO Pos-it-ive! You jus' do the run, Ken, it's the rules, initiation, an' then Crew brothers help Crew brothers.

LAURA I don't believe this!

KANINDA Then you get N'gensi? 50

Afterthought.

See if he does this initiation?

THEO Yeah, I can do anythink. Whenever. The more the better in the Crew. How's about this time tomorrow? After school?

KANINDA	(*nodding*) Okay.	55
THEO	But only when you're in the Crew, man.	

Kaninda looks back along the wall at the run he's got to do.

KANINDA	So I do this run? What is it?	
THEO	See this straight bit of river wall, down to the kids' playground? You run it fast, along the top, which ain't wide, which anyone could walk, slow – but to get in the Crew you run along it like Olympics, an' you do it in under twenny seconds …	60

Kaninda looks along the wall and shrugs.

	Or you don't. You're too slow, or you fall off. Which ain't serious this side of the wall, but that …	65
KANINDA	You are wet. I been in rivers …	
THEO	No, son, you are dead. See, you got to do it at low tide, when all you got twenny foot down is concrete slabs an' old shopping trolleys.	70
KANINDA	Twenty seconds? No problem!	
LAURA	Kaninda! That's suicide!	
THEO	Top dog!	
KANINDA	Then you get Yusulu boy here for the same?	75
THEO	(*walking Kaninda back along the wall, heading offstage*) Pos-it-ive!	

Kaninda kicks off his shoes and starts taking deep breaths. Sergeant Matu appears in his spot.

SERGEANT MATU	Pump up! Pump up! You got me? Oxygen! Two full lungs of it! Rope bridges, trees across water, keep your eyes ahead on 80 where you're goin' an' trust your feet. Pump up! I'm telling you. Oxygen for speed and fast blood for clear eyes.

Sergeant Matu disappears.

KANINDA	(*looks over the river wall*) Long way down!
THEO	You reckon N'gensi could do this an' all? 85

Kaninda shrugs and walks off by the wall.

(*to Baz Rosso*) Got your stop watch?

BAZ ROSSO	Don't need no stop watch, I can count.
THEO	(*shouts off to Kaninda*) That's it, man! Start there!
LAURA	He can fall! He can kill himself! 90
THEO	Lor, girl, I done it! I'm Crew!
LAURA	But you're stupid! This is stupid. **Initiation**!
THEO	Yeah, jus' like christenin'!

He calls to Kaninda, who is offstage.

You ready, Ken. Be hot, man!

LAURA	Really stupid! 95

Laura covers her eyes as Baz Rosso raises his hand.

BAZ ROSSO	(*calls*) You ready?
THEO	(*calls*) Do the business, Ken!
LAURA	(*calls*) Be careful!
BAZ ROSSO	(*calls, sweeping down his arm*) Then, go! **Avanti**! 100

THEO   (*calls*) Go, man!

LAURA   (*calls*) Watch out!

She screams at a stumble.

THEO   (*calls*) You're all right, that's it, son. Keep
        straight. You're doin' good!

To Baz.

Watch, he's quick! Half way!   105

Calls.

Go on, man.

To Laura.

Look at that balance!

LAURA   Look at that idiot!

THEO   Go on! Go on!

Kaninda runs into view.

BAZ ROSSO   Fifteen …   110

LAURA   You've done it! Stop now, stop!

THEO   Great, Ken! You're sool, you!

KANINDA Yusulu?

*He is suddenly thrown off guard, looks around for
Faustin N'gensi, and loses his footing.*

BAZ ROSSO   Eighteen …

LAURA   Kaninda!   115

She rushes forward and grabs at him.

THEO   Ken!

Kaninda falls off the wall on the river side, but he is saved by Laura's hands that have grabbed his arm.

LAURA   Help! Help me!

Theo and Baz Rosso help her to haul him over to safety.

THEO   Pos-it-ive, Laura! You was quick!

BAZ ROSSO   Twenty! **Vincitore**! You made it, boy!

THEO   Great! You're in, Ken, you're in the   120
Crew! See?

KANINDA   (*looking round urgently*) Where's Yusulu?
You said Yusulu.

THEO   I said you're sool, you – which you are,
man. Real sool!   125

BAZ ROSSO   So, tomorrow we talk tactics and strategy.
Uh? I'll see you. **Ciao**!

He goes.

THEO   Ciao, man!

LAURA   Ye Gods, Kaninda!

Kaninda bows to Laura and formally shakes her hand.

KANINDA   I thank you. For that.   130

LAURA   That's all right. Take a life, save a life.

But Kaninda isn't listening to her.

KANINDA   (*to Theo*) Here. Tomorrow. Now you get
him? Yusulu.

THEO   Sure, 'cos you're in. We're brothers.

He puts an arm round Theo's shoulder.

C'mon. I'll nick you a Coke off Mal.   135

He walks Kaninda off, but over his shoulder he says to Laura …

Cheers, Lor. Cheers for fixin' it.

Kaninda looks round at Laura as he's led off, wiping his mouth with the back of his hand, like smudging lipstick.

KANINDA   Laura?

Scene 3

'Captain' Betty Rose's kitchen. Betty Rose is preparing the dinner. Laura comes in with a bag of potatoes, which she starts peeling. Betty Rose has picked up a newspaper for Laura to put her peelings in and is reading it.

BETTY ROSE   Violence! Sweet Jesus, Lord, what next?

Laura knows what she is reading and nervously steadies herself at the table.

Joy-ridin' and knockin' down a kid, an' all. Round here.   140

She reads on.

An' drivin' off! What next, Lord, what next?

LAURA   Perhaps they didn't know what they'd done …

BETTY ROSE   Didn't know? How could you didn't know you'd done such a thing like that? An' what   145 was they doin' in the car in the first place, racin' round the streets? 'Didn't know what they was doin'!'

LAURA   People sometimes do stuff they're ashamed of … Accidentally.   150

BETTY ROSE   Accidentally!? They knew what they was doin'; it ain't like knockin' over a glass o' water!

In her tension Laura accidentally knocks a jug over, but steadies it.

They knew, an' they deserve God's punishment, don't care who they are.   155
(*Significantly.*) I don' want them sort goin' up to my heaven, I tell you.

LAURA   But God forgives, doesn't He? He'd forgive them, wouldn't He, if they were repentant?   160

BETTY ROSE   For this!? I wouldn't, I can't see it. An' what's this 'they'?

She looks at the paper.

There's no 'they' about it. S'pose I read it too quick.

She gets on; too busy.

The trash who'd do such a thing! It's   165
hell-fire for that one, an' all, sure as God's my maker!

Laura takes up her peeler again, but it clatters to the floor. She runs out of the room.

Scene 4

*The riverfront by the Thames Sailing Club. Kaninda
is on a jetty. He walks along it, sees something he's
looking for, lies down on the jetty, pulls at a rope
and draws a small boat nearer. Kaninda is pleased
at his find and he pushes the boat away. He stands
up and looks over at the sugar ship as if measuring
the distance. Laura, made-up and looking somehow
older, comes to the jetty but hides herself before
she can be seen by Kaninda.*

KANINDA   Oars. Oars, just.

For the first time in London, he smiles.

Scene 5

*A river in Lasai. The scene becomes the Lasain
river, the sugar ship no longer in view. (With a
foliage gobo, Kaninda, in neutral clothing, can
become a soldier.) Sergeant Matu comes along
the jetty with a boatman and joins Kaninda.*

BOATMAN   (*to Sergeant Matu*) I'm not in your war.
I'm not Kibu and I'm not Yusulu. From   170
the Ugandan shore, me.

SERGEANT MATU   Maybe! But you've got jus' the boat I need.

Referring to Kaninda ...

This soldier an' me is looking for a cache
of weapons up river, the next village. He's
light, I pole, he looks out for crocs an'   175
Yusulu, you got me? You're not involved,
only your boat, just.

BOATMAN No. Sorry, captain. This is not my war.

He ropes the boat in and pulls from it a net of small river fish.

I stay clean for both sides.

He pushes the boat away and walks off.

SERGEANT MATU (*to Kaninda*) Not the end of it. Cigarettes. 180
What he's fishing for is cigarettes. Two or
three packets, you got me? Unhitch that
boat an' wait.

He follows the boatman off. Kaninda unties the boat and holds it to the jetty. Sergeant Matu returns.

No problem.

KANINDA The boatman said yes? 185

SERGEANT MATU He's content. We go!

He gets down into the boat.

Push me off. Wait there while I teach this
pole what to do.

Kaninda pushes the boat off.

Scene 6

The riverfront by the Thames Sailing Club. Laura appears from where she has been lurking.

LAURA Now I know what you're up to. You're
going to do a run. You're on your toes … 190

Kaninda stares at her.

You've got a plan to get away – lucky you!

Laura suddenly grabs Kaninda, crying and shaking. He is like a stick at first, but as she cries he bends to her.

Lucky, lucky you.

KANINDA   Comfort.

But it's his comfort he's talking about.

Laura …

He kisses the tears on her cheeks.

LAURA   (*pulling away*) No. I'm sorry. We mustn't.   195
Kaninda, I wish I had a plan. Right now
I don't know what I'm doing, where I'm
going, what I'm up to.

KANINDA   Troubles, you got?

LAURA   Troubles I got. Look at me! All dressed up   200
for running off, hitching a lift in a lorry
somewhere – but I've got no plan how.

Kaninda puts a hand on her shoulder.

KANINDA   (*looking across at the sugar ship and
back again*) What troubles you got?

LAURA   Big troubles.

She waves them away.

And Kaninda, I didn't know about the run.   205

KANINDA   Gets me what I want, just.

Kaninda takes a tissue from his pocket with which he wipes the tears from Laura's cheeks.

LAURA   (*staring at Kaninda she has a sudden change of mind*) No, I'd better go back.

She takes the tissue from Kaninda.

But I can't go back home like this, can I?

She cleans off her make-up with her own tears.

Thank you, Kaninda.

KANINDA   (*helping her*) It's me who thanks.   210

LAURA   You're not upset about what I did to you?

Kaninda shakes his head, shrugs.

KANINDA   I thank you always.

LAURA   Always? For saving you?

Breaking away, looking across at the ship.

I've made up my mind, Kaninda. When you go off on your ship to Mozambique, on   215
whatever tide …

KANINDA   Who said this?

LAURA   … I'm coming with you.

Scene 7

Victoria Comprehensive School lavatories. Faustin is washing his hands at the sinks. Theo comes up to him.

THEO   Hey, Foz, man, you on your own?

FAUSTIN   (*nervously looking round*) Teacher …   220

THEO   He's outside, standin' guard, you're all
right. Told him I had to go, urgent!

Faustin takes this seriously; no smile.

Not really. Wanted a word. What I meant,
are you on your own where you live? No
brothers with you, an' that?   225

Faustin shakes his head.

(*standing at the urinal*) So, you phone
home, do you, like, Africa? Or ain't you
got no one to phone to – an' that's why
you're here, sort o' thing …

FAUSTIN Got a sister …   230

THEO   Yeah? Where? In London? Livin' wi'
someone else?

FAUSTIN Somewhere, now. But not in London – in
Lasai, convent school. Don't know where.
We split up in the fighting, after …   235

THEO   Tough, man. Like, I had one an' all, a sister.
Once. Only, Mal, my big brother, works
for this phone shop in Deptford. EezeeKall.
Y'know, cheap calls to the Caribbean, an'
Nigeria, Ghana, where you come from …   240

FAUSTIN Lasai?

THEO   Yeah, all that. Sort of, if you wanted to get
in his shop to phone places, like your
missin' persons, Red Cross, convents, put
word out about your sister – long calls an'   245
not ritzy priced – I reckon Mal can swing
it. Or fax. Pos-it-ive.

FAUSTIN   Your brother?

THEO   Yeah, only, I don' suppose your ol' lady
where you live gives you the run of the   250
phone, does she? See, it all helps my
brother in the slack time. Worth a go,
i'nt it?

FAUSTIN   I need finding her. Just to know she's
okay …   255

THEO   Tell you what, come down my place
tonight an' I'll give you the **rip-off**. Then
it's down to you what you do.

FAUSTIN   What place?

THEO   Where I live. Down the Barrier Estate.   260
Over there; not far.

FAUSTIN   You can't bring this rip-off to school?

THEO   No, you gotta talk to Mal. He does the deals.
I'll meet you my place. Pioneer
House, anyone'll tell you. Half five.   265

FAUSTIN   I think, yes. Thank you.

*He goes out. A crowd of other boys are let in.
Ad lib words of relief as they all face the wall.*

THEO   (*to one of them*) Cheers, Tucker.

BOY 1   Wha' for?

THEO   Tellin' us about his sister.

He beckons Faustin.

Hey! Foz!   270

He walks him into the next scene.

Scene 8

The Thames Barrier riverfront, where Kaninda did his run. Kaninda enters like a tracker behind Theo and Faustin, skirts them to be in front of them and hides himself by the river wall. Faustin walks tentatively, Theo dancing and jigging round him.

THEO   Dunno where he is. Mal's gotta be here in a minute. Down here, Foz. Pos-it-ive.

FAUSTIN Where?

THEO   Down here.

Suddenly Kaninda leaps out, stands facing Faustin.

KANINDA Yusulu!   275

FAUSTIN No!

KANINDA You die!

THEO   Ken!

KANINDA (*to Theo*) Go! Go – or you too!

THEO   I ain't here, man, I ain't here!   280

He runs off.

FAUSTIN No! Leave me! I'm here just the same as you!

KANINDA Not the same as me! I'm Kibu, you're Yusulu.

FAUSTIN And both with no families. I'm not a   285
        fighter, me. You can kill me, easy. But I'm …
        still … just the same as you …

KANINDA It's okay you got no family. Because why?
        You are enemy! Yusulu!

FAUSTIN   I didn't start it! You didn't start it. I'm me,   290
           just me. I'm victim, the same as you …

KANINDA   Not the same as me! I'm soldier. I live.
           You're enemy, you are dead!

FAUSTIN   No! Please!

*Kaninda leaps at Faustin and gets a fierce grip on
Faustin's shoulder.*

Off! Get off!   295

*Kaninda kicks sideways at Faustin's legs and has
him prone on the ground, jumping up and crashing
down with a knee on Faustin.*

(*fighting back*) Stop! No!

*Kaninda grabs Faustin's hair, pulls his head up
and punches him. Faustin groans and is whoozy.*

KANINDA   Kill Yusulu! You die!

*Kaninda hauls Faustin to his feet and stands him
against the river wall; then with one hand at the
neck and the other under the knee he goes to lift
Faustin over, into the drop.*

Down! Down, you go!

FAUSTIN   No! No! Please, no!

Theo runs back.

THEO   Neg-a-tive, Ken!   300

He pulls Kaninda off Faustin.

I got enough blood on my hands already,
I ain't dancin' to this rap.

*Faustin rolls back off the wall, gets to his knees,
then to his feet. Suddenly he finds the strength to
run off.*

KANINDA (*to Theo*) Traitor!

THEO (*blocking Kaninda's way from following
Faustin*) Sorry, Ken, but I ain't havin' it ...

*Kaninda advances on Theo, who is backing off fast,
palms up in pleading, till he suddenly turns and
runs off himself, Olympic fast. Kaninda drops his
hands and stands there panting, staring after Theo.
Suddenly, he spits at the ground where Theo had
stood. Laura enters.*

LAURA Kaninda! I've been looking for you.   305
We've got some planning to do before
Saturday night. Provisions.

She sees the state Kaninda is in.

Have you been in a fight?

KANINDA Always fight, me.

LAURA Who with?   310

Kaninda shrugs.

Food. We'll need to take food, the sort of
stuff the ex-army shops sell. You know,
those places that sell uniform and boots
and camouflage tents; they sell iron
rations. For survival. And water tablets.   315

KANINDA Steal from the ship. Everything is there.

He suddenly shakes his head at her.

It's hard for girls. You got family, not like me ...

LAURA   Family, but I haven't got God. So when you get back to Lasai to fight your war, I 320 can do good works for the people. Care. And if I do that for long enough, doing good, sacrificing myself, I've got to have a good chance of being forgiven, haven't I?

A deep breath.

What time do we go?   325

KANINDA   (*shrugs*) In the dark.

LAURA   We row across to the ship in that little boat ... we climb the rope ...

KANINDA   We go in, like rats.

LAURA   Yeah, like rats. Do rats go up to heaven, 330 do you think?

KANINDA   (*shrugs*) It's here counts, just.

Sergeant Matu appears in his spot.

SERGEANT MATU   Go alone, you got me? Regiment disintegrated, platoon done for – you go alone, soldier! Survival, you don't need no 335 other mouth to feed, safety, you don't need no other mouth to squawk, mental, you don't need no weak'ning voice in your ear. Double the runners an' you double the danger. Run an' hide alone! 340 Look to yourself – get back and regroup – an' every chance along the way you kill Yusulu! But a soldier's his only best friend when he's on the run.

His spot goes in a slow fade. Baz Rosso,
Theo and some other Crew come along.

THEO	Lor, girl!	345

BAZ ROSSO (*snapping his fingers*) You! Ken, uh? I
want you! The Federation war …

CREW BOY 1 Yeah!

Spits on the ground with relish.

The war!

BAZ ROSSO I'm calling up the Crew, an' you're one of   350
the Crew, an' I'm calling you up, uh?

THEO Sure, Baz, he's in. He's hot, this man! See
him just now with that kid …

BAZ ROSSO Well, that's good news, Theo. Good news.
'Cos if your hot man blows out, it won't   355
be me he's lettin' down no more, it'll
be all the Crew – him bein' a member …

KANINDA (*patronisingly*) Crew war?

BAZ ROSSO An' if he doesn't fight, it won't be just
him who suffers, uh? Next o' kin, that's   360
where we hit traitors …

He suddenly grabs Laura and holds her in a neck
lock.

No, it wouldn't be just you, Ken – you let
us down an' we cut the girl.

THEO Lor? What you on about, man?

LAURA Get off!   365

BAZ ROSSO	(*lets Laura go*) I'm on about winnin' this war. No one comes on my estate an' kicks the likes of Little Jackson. Uh?
THEO	Yeah, pos-it-ive, Baz! But—
CREW BOYS	Yeah! 370
	Right on!
	Main man!
BAZ ROSSO	So you be sure, sunshine. You're in – or she's ugly! For life!

Kaninda looks from one to another, and finally at Laura.

KANINDA	What you want? In your war? I do it. 375
THEO	Good man, Ken!
CREW BOY 1	Yeah, son!
BAZ ROSSO	(*to Theo*) You get razzlin' at school tomorrow. I want everyone called up.
THEO	Sure, man. 380
BAZ ROSSO	An' I'll do the plannin'. Only thing is – when?
KANINDA	No. Where, first.
BAZ ROSSO	Where? Down there, where d'you think? Their streets, pay 'em out where all their 385 people can see they don' mess wi' Crew.
KANINDA	No. Not there. They know, there. All the places, their hiding, the best ambush, enemy knows there, good …
BAZ ROSSO	Well, I know down there an' all, uh? It's 390 only along the river, or through that bit of the town.

THEO	Or here, then, man – eh? We know our patch like they know theirs We wait for 'em to come an' we skin 'em down our Barrier, an' over they go into the Mississippi. Pos-it-ive!

395

KANINDA	(*crouching, thinking*) No. Not here. Through your town.

*He points at an imaginary map
on the paving.*

Start there, just, where they live, only   400
some men, not all. Pretend being beaten,
run off, back through the town, they come
after: then the others – ambush!

CREW BOY 2	Down the town?
CREW BOY 1	With all them people about?

405

KANINDA	Best. People help, rebels attack at the marketplace. Full with children, old people, bags, carts, bicycles, fright, surprise. Disorder!
THEO	Confusion!

410

KANINDA	Confusion wins!
BAZ ROSSO	I can see that. Divide an' rule.
KANINDA	Escape is easy. In the crowd.
BAZ ROSSO	Yeah, that'll be it. Down the town. We'll decoy them off their estate, an' wham! So that makes the 'when' an' all, don' it?

415

CREW BOY 1	How come, Baz?
BAZ ROSSO	Got to be Saturday. Everyone's down the town Saturday.

420

LAURA	(*concerned*) Even the Silver Bells!	
THEO AND OTHERS	Yeah!	
	Too right!	
	We'll stuff 'em!	
	Can't wait!	425
BAZ ROSSO	Full Crew! Fight!	
CREW BOYS AND THEO	Fight! Fight! Fight!	

Scene 9

Federation Street. Dusk. The Federation gang is gathered. Queen Max has got her carrier bag of powder hair colouring.

QUEEN MAX	(*giving out cans of hair colouring*) Here you are, share these round.	
CHARLIE TY	Wha's this?	430
QUEEN MAX	Hair dust, different colours.	
SNUFF	Wha' for?	
QUEEN MAX	What d'you think? Spray it on your hair, then we're all red, blue or green heads, **doz**! Till you brush it out quick. If Old Bill gets involved it messes up the witness statements. But don' get nicked. None of you. This is for our Dolly. Right?	435
VARIOUS	Yeah!	440
	They won't nick me!	
	I'll die first!	
	Can't wait!	

QUEEN MAX	The meet's tomorrow at the Ropeyard Arms twelve o'clock – an' we march on the Barrier, along the riverfront.

445

SNUFF	Gotcha!

Sing 'Oh when the Fed's go marchin' in ...!'

QUEEN MAX	An' don't no one not be there in their coloured hair.
CHARLIE TY	(*looking at his can*) Ever seen a red-haired Chinese?

450

General laughs, but is shut up by ...

SNUFF	Only when it's fresh blood!

Scene 10

The Barrier Estate, riverfront. Members of the Crew are there – including Baz Rosso, Theo and Kaninda. We can hear a police helicopter in the distance and the heightening music of a snare drum.

BAZ ROSSO	Right, Saturday, today's the day! No weapons, you hear me? We're goin' in the town in a bit. Hoods up an' wear your heavy boots – it's a good kickin' we're givin' 'em, for what Little Jackson got.

455

THEO	Carry nothin', man?
BAZ ROSSO	(*taking a big stone out of his pocket*) One o' these in your fist, or a bunch o' keys through your fingers. But nothin' you can't drop without gettin' **sussed**.

460

CREW BOY 1	So how we gonna know they're coming? I'm in the doorway of the supermarket;

| | how do I know you've got 'em chasing you through the town? | 465 |

| BAZ ROSSO | (*smiling, the great leader, producing a mobile phone*) Courtesy o' Mal Julien. |

| THEO | Don' spread it, man – he don' know! |

| BAZ ROSSO | New sim cards, can't be traced to my number. I got one, an' he's got one. | 470 |

He points to Kaninda.

He's your man to watch for. When he gets word I've got 'em comin', he's gonna give the signal an' you get ready!

| CREW BOY 2 | What signal? | 475 |

Kaninda puts his head back and does a jackal shriek.

| BAZ ROSSO | It's gotta be heard! Then we come runnin' through, an' you wait for 'em to pass, an' come stormin' out of your hidin' places … |

| CREW BOY 1 | An' 'ave 'em! | 480 |

| CREW BOY 2 | Sure thing! 'Ave 'em hard! |

| VARIOUS | Too right! |
| | Justice! |

Someone does a weak jackal shriek; others join in.

| BAZ ROSSO | Right! Shut up! Let's get to this war, uh? | 485 |

He leads them off.

Scene 11

*A pedestrian walkway in South London. A street
sign indicates a hospital nearby. There are various
passers-by, going and coming from visiting. Laura
is in her God's Force uniform, walking towards
the hospital. In her hand is a blue carrier bag.
She stops and looks round to check she can't be
overheard. She stands under the hospital sign,
looks up to heaven and then down at the ground
to disguise her intent.*

LAURA   (*praying*) God, I'm sorry, and I know you've
got no place in your heart for me right now.
But when I do what I'm going to do, going
with Kaninda, when I do Your work in Africa
and serve You – please let me come back   490
into Your almighty kingdom.

Looks around; a change of tack.

But before me, before my immortal soul
even, please save the injured girl in this
hospital. I'm going to say sorry to her,
and goodbye, and then leave her in Your   495
tender loving hands …

As if to a passer-by.

Amen.

*Sharon Slater comes along with something
wrapped in newspaper.*

Sharon! What are you doing here?

SHARON   Been following after you. Thought I'd let
you get clear of your house.   500

71

LAURA	Why?
SHARON	You want this, do you?

She unwraps the number plate.

LAURA	Why should I want it? It's your mum's initials …

SHARON	My dad's doing up my room. My	505
	stepmum'll be into everything. I got some	
	stuff down behind the bath, but I can't	
	lose this nowhere.	

LAURA	Why should I want it? It's not mine.

SHARON	It's your business, though, i'n it? There's	510
	a war on about all this today, an' I'm not	
	gonna get seen slinging it in the river,	
	thanks.	

LAURA	Give it to me, I'll get rid of it for you.

SHARON	No, you get rid of it for you!	515

With meaning …

I'm letting you off the hook.

Laura takes the plate and puts it into her carrier bag.

(*going*) See you!

LAURA	(*when Sharon's out of earshot*) No you won't. Not for a long time.

Laura looks up at the hospital sign and follows in the direction of the arrow, walking into …

Scene 12

*Thames Reach Hospital. Dolly is in a public ward,
in bed propped up on pillows. There are no tubes
or electrical gadgets attached to her now. Another
girl patient, Ashleigh, is in a chair having her
pulse taken by a nurse. Laura comes in. She looks
around, fearful of finding Dolly's family here.*

LAURA	Excuse me. I've come to see Dolly Hedges.	520
ASHLEIGH	Ate some breakfast an' wasn't sick. And talked some more. Getting better, she is.	
LAURA	(*moving over to Dolly's bed, but cautiously*) Is she? So she's … coming out of it?	
NURSE	Signs of improvement. Let's have your temperature, now, Ashleigh.	525

She puts a thermometer in Ashleigh's mouth.

LAURA	(*whispering*) Dolly …
NURSE	(*to Laura*) You can talk to her normally, love. She's been talking to us, haven't you, Dolly?

530

*Leaves the thermometer in Ashleigh's mouth
and comes over.*

And she's changed her record at last.

Plumps up her pillows.

LAURA	(*looking up, very alert*) Changed her record? From what they said in the paper?

NURSE Only one more word, but the rest will
come out now, sure as anything. 535

LAURA What … was the new word?

ASHLEIGH (*takes out the thermometer*) 'Van.'

Pops it back.

NURSE 'Van.' White van – that's what she's
telling us. Must have been what hit her …

LAURA Van? 540

NURSE That's right.

*Ashleigh nods vigorously. The implication of this
begins to dawn on Laura.*

LAURA Not the red car …

NURSE Not the red car.

Moves back to Ashleigh.

Apparently. A white van.

LAURA Dolly! 545

She bends over and kisses Dolly on the cheek.

Oh, God, oh God, thank you, God.

Whispering.

And I'm sorry, Dolly, I'm very sorry. I
thought I'd done it, and I'm sorry …

*She steals backwards away from the bed, then
turns and hurries out of the ward.*

ASHLEIGH She's pleased!

Scene 13

*Outside the Ropeyard Arms, in the street. The
Federation gang is there. Queen Max is dressed like
a warrior queen, her flesh shining with body rub.
Her hair is dusted blue and her boots are long black
lace-ups like a wrestler's. Across her shoulder,
slung like a quiver, is a bag about fifteen inches
long. The other gang members have dusted hair,
but no weapons are in sight, although there are
bulges.*

QUEEN MAX (*to her troops*) Right, you ready? Snuff? 550
    Charlie? Dean? You others? We go to war!
    For Dolly!

VARIOUS Yeah!

    Come on!

    Can't wait! 555

    Let's do the business!

    An' kill!

    The chant is taken up.

ALL Yeah! Kill! Kill! Kill! Kill! Kill!

Scene 14

*The riverfront, approaching the Ropeyard Arms.
Baz Rosso and a few members of the Crew,
including Theo, are coming cautiously along. We
can hear the helicopter hovering in the distance.
We can also hear the Federation's chant of 'Kill!
Kill! Kill! Kill!' coming closer.*

THEO	(*jigging in front of Baz Rosso*) Hey, man, listen!	560
BAZ ROSSO	Uh?	
THEO	Liss-en out!	
FEDERATION	(*off, but nearer*) Kill! Kill! Kill! Kill!	
BAZ ROSSO	They're comin' through …	
CREW BOY 2	(*picking up on the Federation chant*) Kill! Kill! Kill! Kill!	565
THEO	Neg-a-tive, man! Too slow! 'Nih-i-late! 'Nih-i-late! 'Nih-i-late!	

The Crew starts to march off towards the Ropeyard with this faster rhythm.

BAZ ROSSO	Hold on! They're comin'! Hang about!	
THEO	Stand!	570

The Crew stands, still chanting ''Nih-i-late!'

BAZ ROSSO	Be ready! That way!

He points out to the audience, stage right. Queen Max and the Federation come in from stage left, still chanting 'Kill!' She sees the Crew and puts up her hand to halt her people. For a moment the two chants make a sort of counterpoint.

SNUFF	Pathetic loosers! There's only them!
CHARLIE TY	That all you could raise?
QUEEN MAX	He never could raise much!

The chanting on both sides suddenly stops. The lull before the fight begins. Hatred marks every face.

	Hang on – this is some stunt!	575

CHARLIE TY	What stunt?! They're just showin' out – then they're gonna run away an' think they've got it all over …
BAZ ROSSO	Had to bring all these little kids, Max-eene! Leave any infants at home? 580
QUEEN MAX	Get them! Get these worms!

The Federation charge at the Crew.

BAZ ROSSO	(*running, pulling out his mobile*) Too many! Run! **Scappare**!

The Crew runs offstage into the audience, pursued by the Federation.

CREW, VARIOUS	Run!
	Get out of here! 585
	Mum! Help me!
	There's too many of 'em!
FEDERATION, VARIOUS	Chicken!
	Pathetic!
	Kill 'em! 590
	Show 'em!
	This is for our Dolly!

Scene 15

Millennium Mall. The shopping centre on a busy day. Everyone not in the Crew or the Federation is on stage as shoppers, etc. Ad lib shopping conversations. Kaninda and other Crew come in and Kaninda points them to go to different doorways, behind an advertising board, etc.

KANINDA   Crew platoon! Take positions! You there.
Ambush soon. There, just. They run
through, we stand our ground. Hit fast,   595
hit last, an' hit to kill!

*'Captain' Betty Rose in God's Force uniform
comes through with a girl also in uniform carrying
a set of tubular bells and a hammer. She doesn't
see Kaninda.*

BETTY ROSE   We're through there – thought I'd lost you.
God be praised!

*'Captain' Betty Rose and the girl exit. After a while
the sound of the Silver Bells can be heard playing
'Oh, Happy Day'. Kaninda's mobile rings, Bizet's
'Toreador' tune.*

KANINDA   (*in Sergeant Matu's spot*) Stand ready!
You got me?   600

*The Crew are in hiding, standing alert, battle-ready.
The shoppers carry on, unaware. Baz Rosso and
the Crew with him come running from the audience
onto the stage and into the Mall, pursued by
Queen Max and the Federation. The decoy Crew
with Baz Rosso and Theo run on through.*

BAZ ROSSO   Yes! Now! They're comin'!

*Kaninda does the jackal howl and the other Crew
come out of hiding.*

THEO   Hit 'em! Hit 'em hard!

QUEEN MAX   Kill that Rosso!

KANINDA   Attack! Attack!

The Crew have their hoods up; the Federation have
their coloured hair. The fight begins. Shoppers
shout and scream, haul push-chairs to safety.

SHOPPERS, VARIOUS   Get out of it!   605

Little toe-rags!

What's it coming to!?

Granddad!

I'm all right!

Just get away!   610

Watch yourself!

In here! Get in the shop!

Call the police!

Someone call the police!

Where's the law?   615

We need 'em here!

Look to yourself!

Where's Mum? Get Mum! Anyone
seen Mum?

She went in there!   620

Get in there with her!

Little scum! You're scum!

Don't rile 'em!

Scum of the earth!

They're worse'n scum!   625

etc., etc.

The Silver Bells music stops. The fighters on both
sides shout a bit but are mostly intent on the struggle.

CREW AND FEDERATION, VARIOUS	Take one o' these!
	That's for Dolly!
	That's for Little Jackson!
	Come on, come on! Think you're hard?
	Pathetic! 630
	Snag 'em!
	Beat the daylights out!
	Brown-slice 'em!
	Mullah!
	Got any teeth left? 635
	Spit that out!
	Go an' get your mum!
	My nan could do you!
	etc., etc.
BAZ ROSSO	There's still more of them!
CREW BOY 2	I've got me stone! 640
BAZ ROSSO	Stone's no good against this!

*The whole point of this fight is its ugliness.
Some shoppers get involved and hurt – the fight
could spill into the audience to signify innocent
involvement – as one by one the Crew fighters – up
against the numbers of the Federation – go off,
nursing wounds. The whole thing is shaming.*

*At the height of it, Baz Rosso and Queen Max
spot each other – but Queen Max can't get a swing
at Baz Rosso as he grapples with her, and the
wrestling fight continues. Baz Rosso breaks out
and Queen Max pursues him.*

QUEEN MAX	Rosso!

Goes after him.

Come back.

They run off. Charlie Ty singles out Kaninda for an attack.

CHARLIE TY	It's Lucky Luke!
KANINDA	Come! Come!

645

He stands ready in a hand-to-hand stance. Charlie Ty runs at Kaninda, who doesn't turn or run but lets Charlie Ty come. Suddenly Kaninda jumps, his feet one behind the other, throws his forearms across his body and blocks the thrust. The sudden force of it stops Charlie Ty and sends him staggering back. Before he can get his balance, Kaninda boots him in the body.

CHARLIE TY	Aaaah!
KANINDA	Juicy-juicy!

Charlie Ty disappears as Kaninda sees off someone else.

Pull back! Away!

All the Crew except Kaninda and Theo limp, hobble and run off.

THEO	(*at the door of a shop*) In here! Come on, man!

650

Theo runs into the shop, but Kaninda stays to fight, and turns as Charlie Ty and Snuff Bowditch come walking hard and fast towards him.

CHARLIE TY   Kill! Got you, you little rat!

SNUFF   You're dead, son!

Shoppers come to the edges of the battleground, but no one intervenes as Kaninda is trapped at the shop doorway by two more Federation members coming out of the shop behind him. Kaninda again takes up a hand-to-hand defensive stance. But he is clearly out-numbered.

KANINDA   Come! Come!

CHARLIE TY   This is your lot, scum!

SNUFF   'Ave that, you!   655

The four start kicking and punching Kaninda. He starts to put up a spirited defence but they are going to be too much for him.

SHOPPERS, VARIOUS   Look at this lot!

Pathetic!

All they know!

Let 'em hurt each other!

It's what they want!   660

etc., etc. No one goes to help Kaninda.

SNUFF   This is for Charlie!

CHARLIE TY   This is for Snuff! No it ain't, it's for me!

But 'Captain' Betty Rose suddenly comes in and wades into the Federation four.

BETTY ROSE   Get off! Get packin', will you!

*She **scrags** two of the Federation off Kaninda. They fight back, but she punches and slaps her weight and they run off.*

FED 1   (*running*) Watch your back round here!

*'Lieutenant' Peter Rose runs in and hauls Snuff
away from the doorway. Charlie Ty stops for a
moment.*

BETTY ROSE   Kaninda Rose, what the hell is goin' on   665
here? How d'you get involved in this
riff-raff?

PETER ROSE   What are you up to, son?

SNUFF   I ain't fightin' God!

*He runs off. Kaninda still has his eyes on a
possible attack from Charlie Ty.*

CHARLIE TY   I'm gonna kill you!   670

BETTY ROSE   (*walking towards Charlie Ty, who, seeing
the glint in her eye, backs away*) Don't
you dare touch this boy! This boy's in my
keepin', you got me? This is my boy!
He belongs wi' me, an' you hurt one hair
of his head an' I'm goin' to tan your hide!   675

*She goes for her belt. Charlie Ty backs
further away.*

Get off! Go an' have a fight wi' your
conscience.

PETER ROSE   Go on, clear off out of it!

Charlie Ty goes.

BETTY ROSE   Please, God, I'm sorry for my husband's
fightin' talk. But sometimes you've got   680
to do what's necessary for your family,
for your own

She puts an arm round Kaninda.

Eh, boy?

Theo comes out of the shop.

THEO You all right, man? Should've come in
there wi' me. Pos-it-ive! 685

BETTY ROSE (*to Theo*) What you doing, Theodore,
what's goin' on here?

THEO Ken's a mate o' mine. We're down here
for a quick look around an' we're only
sudden in the middle of this mash-up! 690
Ding-dong, vi-o-lence, I hate that stuff!

BETTY ROSE Kaninda, you better get home with me.
Because I ain't runnin' the risk of this
startin' up again. And where's Laura?

KANINDA Not here. Didn't come. 695

BETTY ROSE Well, praise the Lord for that. But you're
mine, too, Kaninda, you hear me? You're
my – how to say this, Lord, so the
boy understands? – you're family, you
belong, you're in my group, my gang, 700
my clan, my tribe. You got me? So let's
get you cleaned up an' **lick-spittled** …
Come on, my special man!

*Kaninda looks round, kicks a stone aside and
decides to follow her. They both exit, Kaninda
clearly thinking on what she has said. Theo looks
around; the coast is now clear and he relaxes.
Shoppers resume shopping.*

THEO Lick-spittled!?

*Laura, still in God's Force uniform and carrying
her plastic bag, comes along, seeing Theo.*

LAURA   (*excited, pleased*) Theo! Theo! Guess   705
what?

THEO   I'll never guess nothin' again! Your
ol' lady, she see off the Federation …

LAURA   That girl, that Dolly. I've been to the
hospital, seen her. She's talking, getting   710
better, and guess what she's said? She said
'Van', 'White van'. It wasn't our car that
hit her, it wasn't ours at all.

THEO   Ssssh! I told you, it was all a blur. Blur, I
said, di'n I?   715

LAURA   And when she said it, I knew she was right;
suddenly I could see it again. I was
driving, and a white van did come out of
a side road and it cut in front, don't know
how I forgot it. But I was concentrating   720
on steering straight and you're looking
down at getting your foot over on the
brake. I can see it clear now, though.
Ours wasn't the only wheels going down
that road. She ran out, you grabbed the   725
wheel, we went round the corner and
swerved and bumped, and the next
thing was, she was lying in the gutter.
But that van cut us up, and it was on
the kerb side, so we couldn't have done   730
it. And if it was a van it had no windows,
so how could she have seen through its
side and through you to call me white?
It was the van that was white all the time!

THEO	Yeah, saw that in the blur.	735
LAURA	We've done wrong, Theo, but it wasn't us who hurt that girl. We've still got to be punished and we're still witnesses. We've still got to go to the police … But—	
THEO	No, man!	740
LAURA	… But we didn't actually do it. I've got my credit back with God – and that Dolly's getting better!	
THEO	That's all my prayin'!	
LAURA	Praying? You, too?	745
THEO	Prayin' we don't get caught.	
LAURA	Theo!	
THEO	Pos-it-ive! I survive my way, you survive yours.	

Baz Rosso comes in, very much the worse for the fight with Queen Max; his hair has some of her blue powder brushed into it.

BAZ ROSSO	Eh? We showed 'em, uh?	750
THEO	Yeah! No, neg-a-tive, Baz – no one showed no one, as it goes.	
BAZ ROSSO	Had to be done, uh? Respect. Gotta have respect.	
LAURA	For yourself. You've got to have respect – for yourself.	755
BAZ ROSSO	Oh, preachy-preachy! Anyhow—	

He turns as Queen Max runs in. Her hair is no longer blue, but her top is torn.

QUEEN MAX	Rosso! I'll finish you for this!
BAZ ROSSO	Showin' yourself again, Max-eene? We showed you!

760

| QUEEN MAX | (*lunging at him*) Showed who, Rosso?! |

In going for Baz Rosso, Queen Max knocks into Laura.

LAURA	Watch out!
THEO	Steady!
QUEEN MAX	Get out the way!

Queen Max sends Laura sprawling. The number plate comes sliding out of her plastic bag.

The number plate! You! The red car! You   765
was in all this!

| LAURA | (*trying to get up*) No, no, it was a white van! |

Queen Max grabs the number plate. She wields it above her head as she chases Laura off stage.

| QUEEN MAX | You little goody-goody! |
| THEO | (*follows Laura and Queen Max off*) Laura! |

770

| BAZ ROSSO | I'll see you! |

He walks off fast.

SHOPPERS, VARIOUS	(*looking off stage*) Stop that!
	Behave, you two!
	Is she alive?
	Stupid gang wars!

775

London ain't safe!

And she's God's Force.

Anyone know First Aid round here?

Queen Max returns and walks unimpeded through the shoppers.

QUEEN MAX   I done it, Dolly, I done it!

Exit. The scene freezes.

Scene 16

Kaninda's bedroom. With an eye to the door, Kaninda is stuffing Laura's blue carrier bag with socks, a jumper and the atlas. We can hear 'Captain' Betty Rose wailing in her own bedroom, a sound similar to the wailing of the Kibu women at the Katonga mine tragedy. Kaninda looks in the direction of her bedroom, pauses, then goes on packing his bag. The wailing stops and becomes crying. Betty Rose comes along the corridor to stand outside Kaninda's door, supported by Peter Rose. They are both wearing their best non-uniform clothes for hospital visiting.

BETTY ROSE   Kaninda? Kaninda?   780

Kaninda hides the bag and comes to the door.

PETER ROSE   We're going to the hospital now. Mrs …
Tante … Betty is going to stay there till …
one way or the other … You can come
with us and I'll bring you home …

KANINDA   I stay here.   785

PETER ROSE   I don't know how long we'll be. Please
God she's going to pull through.

*Betty and Peter Rose go. When he's sure that
they've gone, Kaninda goes to his bed and from
under the pillow he pulls a bottle of water. He puts
the water in the bag. He comes out of his room and
walks off along the corridor into:*

Scene 17

*The Jesus Saves Tearooms. It is evening, the place
is almost empty, just a couple of **cabbies** at a table.
Faustin N'gensi is sitting at a table near the counter
with a waiter's apron on. He is doing homework
and doesn't look up. Cautiously, Kaninda comes
into the cafe, carrying his plastic bag. Kaninda
goes to a table near the door, apparently unseen by
Faustin. Mrs Rickard, a stick of a woman, comes to
the counter with two plates, held in bare hands.*

MRS RICKARD   Steve an' Gary's.

*Mrs Rickard looks at Faustin who seems engrossed
in his homework. She puts a plate down, leans over
the counter and cuffs his head.*

Steve an' Gary's!

She hoicks her head towards table seven.

FAUSTIN   Sorry!   790

He gets up and takes the plates which burn him.

Ow!

MRS RICKARD   Soft Samuel!

89

*She throws a cloth at Faustin. Faustin uses the
cloth to carry the plates to the cabbies. From the
pocket of his apron he takes a waiter's order form.
He walks over to Kaninda, who is sitting with his
bag beneath the table. Faustin shows no surprise
at seeing him.*

FAUSTIN   Theo told you where I am? So, you
            here for eating or for killing?

            He takes another step forward to stand closer.

            I know what you can do.   795

            Kaninda stares up at him.

            You think I killed your family? You think
            I blame you for my family? Yusulu,
            Kibu, Nyanga, Banyarwanda, Tutsi,
            Bakongo – tribal is political, boy. Them
            and us, you and me, chiefs and followers.   800
            But not really you and me, not us
            ourselves – it's the leaders make it that way.

            *Under the table we see Kaninda change the
            position of his feet, ready for a lunge.
            Mrs Rickard comes in with a plate of bread
            and butter.*

MRS RICKARD   Bread and butter.

            But Faustin doesn't look round.

FAUSTIN   You kill me for your family revenge; but
            my family was killed the worst way.   805
            Atrocity. No mistake, boy, I hate – but
            I don't hate you. You are three hundred
            miles from me. Tribal war did it, not you.

War takes us all in its hand and smashes
us on the ground.   810

MRS RICKARD   Bread and butter! I'll send you back
where you came from, boy, if you can't
be more useful.

FAUSTIN   (*ignoring her*) I got a sister to find one day.

*One of the cabbies goes to the counter and takes
the bread and butter himself.*

Twin sister. My twin, half of me. They   815
did worse than kill her, boy. She was tied
up and beaten and left in a ditch like
dead meat. But not Kibu.

Kaninda stares his surprise.

Not Kibu, not Yusulu, not tribe. Soldiers.
Men. Individuals. Creatures. Atrocity is   820
not tribal, it is animal. The dead were the
lucky ones. Now she's mind sick in some
convent. Somewhere …

Kaninda looks away.

But you do it, boy.

He tears off his apron to present an easier target.

I'm not running from you for ever. They   825
all commit atrocity. What is one more
atrocity?

*Kaninda looks at Faustin again, holds the moment.
Finally, with Faustin ready for an attack, he lays one
hand on the table cloth and with the other he picks
up the order pad where it has fallen on the cloth
and gives it to Faustin.*

KANINDA   Big supper. Big, to travel on.

Faustin walks to the counter and off.

Scene 18

*The riverfront by the Thames Sailing Club.
It is dark. Kaninda, carrying the blue plastic
bag, comes to the jetty. He looks across at
the lights on the superstructure of the sugar
ship, which hoots, getting ready to depart on
the tide. He bends to pull the boat towards
him. But standing on the boat is Sergeant
Matu.*

Scene 19

*A river in Lasai. The scene changes to Lasai as
Sergeant Matu steps from the boat carrying an
armful of rifles.*

SERGEANT MATU   We done good, soldier. These we can use,
you got me?   830

*Kaninda just watches him. We're not sure which
scene Kaninda is in.*

An' what did it cost us?

KANINDA   Three packets of cigarettes.

Sergeant Matu laughs.

SERGEANT MATU   That's war, boy, that's tribal war.

*Sergeant Matu walks off with Kaninda looking
after him, horrified.*

Scene 20

The riverfront by the Thames Sailing Club. Theo Julien comes along the jetty.

THEO   Ken! You seen Laura, how is she, man?

Kaninda shrugs.

She's too good to go to heaven.   835
She'll be hunky, I reckon.

KANINDA   (*nodding*) A good person.

After a moment's thought.

Not Crew, not Federation. Not Kibu, not
Yusulu. Not black, not white. A person.
Just … a person.   840

THEO   (*not understanding Kaninda*) Yeah, s'pose
you're right. So, what you doin' here?

Not serious.

Goin' for a boat ride?

*Kaninda looks down at the boat and over at the
sugar ship. He does a 360-degree turn, looking
at London.*

KANINDA   Neg-a-tive. Home. I'm goin' home.

*He walks off the jetty and offstage, watched by
Theo. The already darkened stage fades to pitch
black.*

Curtain.

QUESTIONS AND ACTIVITIES

Questions

Keeping track

> **Learning outcomes**
>
> You will:
> - learn who the main character is
> - keep track of the main events in the play
> - express your own ideas on what the play is about and the themes it deals with.
>
> You will do this by reading the play aloud in your class, and stopping every now and then to discuss your reaction to the story and the characters. You will also make brief notes in answer to some questions that will help you 'keep track'.

1   Think about the play's settings.

   a Look at Bernard Ashley's notes on page **v** about staging *Little Soldier*. What ideas does he give you about the kind of play this will be?

   b Think about the number of scenes the play has. (There are 40 in total, split into two acts.)

   i Where do you think the play's events take place?

   ii What do you think will be the main action or plot?

2   Now think about the characters. It is important before you start reading the play to get some idea of their backgrounds and the different groups they belong to. The cast list on page **vi–1** details everyone who appears in the play. Study it, then copy and complete the table on page 95.

Main character	Background	Age	Group/Gang identity
Kaninda Bulumba	African (Lasai)	13	Kibu tribe
Laura Rose	Anglo-Seychellois	13	God's Force
Theo Julien			Barrier Crew
Faustin N'gensi	African (Lasai)		Yusulu tribe
Betty Rose			God's Force
Peter Rose	English	45	
Queen Max			Federation Gang
Baz Rosso	Anglo-Italian		
Snuff Bowditch			
Charlie Ty			
Sergeant Matu	African (Lasai)		
Mal Julien			—
Lydia Becky			
Gifty		10	
Sharon Slater			—
Dolly Hedges			—
Rene Hedges			—

3   Answer the following questions, which relate to Act One,
     Scenes 1–20.

Staging

- The pre-scene (Act One, page 3) is heard but not seen. What
  do you think is happening in it?
- The first thing the audience sees is 'a pile of four bodies'.
  They 'all seem dead'. Which three are dead? Which one
  survives?
- Who seems to be responsible for these deaths?

Kaninda

- When Kaninda arrives in London, he goes to live with Peter and Betty Rose. What organisation do they belong to? Why do you think they are taking Kaninda into their home?
- How does Kaninda feel about his 'new home'?
- What evidence is there that Kaninda's thoughts turn frequently to his former life in the African country of Lasai?
- Sergeant Matu appears in several 'flashbacks'. Who is he? Why do you think Kaninda recalls him so vividly?

The gangs

- Who are the 'Federation' and the 'Crew'?
- How are we shown that they are very hostile to each other?

Dolly

- What causes the accident to Dolly?
- What is she able to tell the police about it?
- How and why does Dolly's accident stir up strong feelings in the Federation gang? What do you predict this could lead to?

Lasai

- What are the main differences between Kaninda's new school, Victoria Comprehensive, and the school he went to in Lasai?
- What terrible incident happened at the school in Lasai? Who caused it?
- How has this incident affected Kaninda?
- When Kaninda finds out about Faustin, the 'new boy' who has also come to Victoria Comprehensive, what happens? Why?

Laura

- How does Laura react to the car accident she helped to cause?
- How is her reaction different from Theo's?

4   Now answer these questions, which are about Act Two, Scenes 1–10.

Joining the crew

- Why does Kaninda agree to become a member of the Crew gang?
- What test does he have to pass in order to qualify?
- Who helps Kaninda during his test? Does he pass it?

Kaninda

- What is Kaninda's 'plan' in Act Two, Scene 6.
- What does Laura tell Kaninda about her plan?
- What happens between Kaninda and Faustin in Act Two, Scene 8?
- What does Faustin tell Kaninda about the tribal war in Lasai between the Kibu and the Yusulu? How does his attitude to it differ from Kaninda's?

Baz Rosso

- What is Baz Rosso planning? Why is Kaninda important to his plans?
- Kaninda agrees to go along with Baz's plans. Why?

5   The final set of questions for you to answer is about Act 2, Scenes 11–20.

Laura

- How does the Ford Escort's number plate come into Laura's possession?
- How does Laura react to the news that Dolly is coming out of her coma and has added the word 'van' to 'white'?

The fight

- During the gang fight in the Millennium Mall (Act Two, Scene 15), Kaninda finds himself in charge of the Crew's tactics. Whose way of speaking does he imitate when he is giving orders?

- The playwright puts in a stage direction in Act Two, Scene 15 that describes the gang fight as 'shaming'. What do you think are the most 'shaming' things about it?
- Who ends the gang fight before those who are fighting intend it to stop?

Laura

- When Laura is speaking to Theo in Act Two, Scene 15, she is deeply relieved. Why? Why do you think she says: 'We've still got to go to the police'?
- How and why does Laura get viciously attacked in Act Two, Scene 15?

Kaninda's changes

- In Act Two, Scene 17, Kaninda sets out to murder Faustin. What does Faustin tell him that makes Kaninda change his mind?
- In Act Two, Scene 19, the playwright's stage direction reads: 'We're not sure which scene Kaninda is in.' What point do you think the playwright is making here?
- What does Kaninda learn about 'tribal war' from the voice of Sergeant Matu?
- At the very end of the play, Kaninda changes. He says about Laura: 'A good person. Not Crew, not Federation. Not Kibu, not Yusulu. Not black, not white. A person. Just ... a person.' What has Kaninda finally learned, and who has been responsible for him learning it?

What have I learnt?

- How has 'Keeping track' helped you to think about the different characters and the relationships between them?
- What have you learnt about using evidence to support your ideas?

ACTIVITIES

Activity 1: Kaninda's story

Learning outcomes

You will:

- explore the character of Kaninda
- organise and present your ideas
- make decisions and select evidence to support your decisions and ideas
- write three accounts of Kaninda's experiences.

You will do this by tracing Kaninda's story in the course of the play.

1   Copy and complete an enlarged version of the chart below.

Kaninda in Africa	Kaninda in London at the Rose's home and at school	Kaninda and the Crew and Federation gangs	Kaninda and Faustin
• He hates the Yusulu tribe because ...	• He dislikes living with the Rose family because ...	• He joins the Crew gang because ...	• He wants to kill Faustin because ...
• He is trained by Sergeant Matu of the Kibu rebel army to ...	• He will not co-operate with his tutor, Miss Mascall, because ...	• He looks down on the gangs' 'war' because ...	• When he listens to Faustin in Act Two, Scene 17, he starts to think ...
• Until the end of the play, he wants to return to Lasai because ...	• At the end of the play, he sees Laura in a new light because ...	• At the end of the play, he regrets taking part in the gang fight because ...	• At the end of the play, he stops seeing Faustin as a Yusulu and starts seeing him as ...

2   Compare your completed chart with others in your class. Then use them to talk about:

- the main ways in which Kaninda *changes* by the end of the play
- the main reasons for the changes in his character and outlook.

3   **By yourself**, write three paragraphs.

- The first should describe Kaninda's experiences in Africa.
- The second should describe how these experiences influence his behaviour when he moves to London.
- The final paragraph should describe, how, by the end of the play, Kaninda throws off the influence of what happened to him in Africa.

You should quote from the play to support the most important points you make.

What have I learnt?

- What have you learnt about how Kaninda develops as a character?
- How did selecting material from the text help you to answer a particular question?
- What have you learnt about why it is important to quote when writing about a play?

Activity 2: Role-play

Learning outcomes

You will:

- explore specific characters
- plan and present your ideas.

You will do this by participating in a role-play (involving the Crew and Federation gangs) that takes place shortly after the play ends.

Imagine that the injuries to Dolly and Laura have made the two gangs decide to call a truce. They meet on 'neutral ground', at the God's Force Citadel, to conduct peace talks.

1   In groups allocate parts for your role-play. There should be an equal number of Crew and Federation gang members: these include Baz Rozzo and Theo (Crew), and Queen Max and Charlie Ty (Federation). Betty Rose is in charge of the meeting.

2   In your groups, plan and make notes on what you will say in the role-play. (The role-play should last between 5 and 10 minutes.) Avoid writing out your lines – jot down prompts only. The Crew role-players should separate from those acting as Federation gang members. You should consider the following.

- The fight at the Millennium Mall. How did you feel when it was happening? How do you feel about it now?
- What happened to Laura. Who was to blame? Has her serious injury changed your mind about gang fighting?
- Why the Crew and the Federation started fighting their 'war' in the first place and have kept on doing so. What, exactly, have they been fighting about? Are they going to be able to stop?

Remember, you are acting out peace talks. Sometimes these can go wrong if people don't want to listen to the other side's point of view.

3   To help you prepare for the role-play consider the following questions.

- How do you think your character would act in this situation? For example, would they be angry or willing to listen to the other gang's point of view?
- How would they show their emotions? For example, would they sit with their arms folded or pace around angrily?
- How would they say their lines? For example, would they say them calmly or shout them?

4   Decide who will speak first and make sure that everyone in your group speaks at least twice.

5   Now, in your groups, you are ready to act out the role-play. Your teacher, in role as Betty Rose, will start the peace talks.

What have I learnt?

- How did performing help you to gain an understanding of the characters and their issues?
- What have you learnt about the skills needed in role-play and how good you are at it?
- What have you learnt about teenage violence and the reasons why it is widespread nowadays?

Activity 3: A newspaper report

Learning outcomes

You will:

- develop analytical skills
- use evidence from the play to present your ideas
- study other texts to understand how they work
- write for a specific audience, with a specific purpose.

You will do this by using details of the play to write a newspaper report on the accident that seriously injured Dolly.

1   Look at Act One, Scene 20, where Laura reads the headline of a news report: 'HIT AND RUN. EVIL OF THE CAR WITH NO PLATES.' Imagine you are a journalist. Plan the report that follows this headline. Imagine you know the *whole* of the story up to Act One, Scene 20. You will need to make brief notes on the following.

- The red Ford Escort was a stolen car. How did it come to be stolen in the first place and who stole it? (Act One, Scene 6.)
- Why did the Ford Escort have no number plates?
- Who was in the car when the accident happened? How did the car come to be in their possession?
- Who was driving? Why will this make headline news?
- Where did the accident happen?
- What is Dolly's condition in hospital? (Act One, Scene 20.)

2   Read several reports from your local newspaper involving crime. Discuss:

- headlines (how do they make a strong impression on the reader?)
- first paragraphs (what information do they give?)
- interviews (how do they add detail and 'human interest' to the story?)

- language (how does the choice of language make the story sound dramatic?)
- presentational devices (how do they add to the impact of the story?).

3 Use your notes from 1 (on page 103) to plan and write the newspaper report for the *Thames Reach Gazette*. Include interviews with Rene Hedges and the police officer investigating the case. Make up your own headline. If possible, produce your final version on computer. Are there any ways you could make it look like a real newspaper page – for example, by using a large heading, a photograph and a caption?

What have I learnt?

- How did reading other newspaper reports help you to write your own?
- What skills did you need to plan and write a newspaper report?

Activity 4: The playwright's presentation of Laura

Learning outcomes

You will:

- explore the character of Laura
- organise and present your ideas
- hold a formal debate with your class.

You will do this by considering how the playwright presents the character of Laura. Then you will decide how far you agree with Theo, who describes her as 'too good to go to heaven'.

1   In pairs, read aloud the scenes listed below in which Laura plays a prominent part. The same person should always read Laura. Their partner should read Theo, Kaninda, etc. There are never more than two people speaking. Read with as much expression as you can, as if you were performing the play on stage. (For example, if your character is being secretive they might whisper and look behind them before they talk.)

- Act One, Scenes 6–8 (pages 10–14)

| *from* | Theo | Laura! Wotcha Lor! |
| *to* | Theo | Go on, turn right, down there. |

- Act One, Scene 13 (pages 24–6)

| *from* | Theo | Well, little Lor! |
| *to* | | the end of the scene. |

- Act One, Scene 20 (pages 42–5)
- Act Two, Scene 6 (pages 56–8)
- Act Two, Scene 8 (pages 63–4)

| *from* | Laura | Kaninda! I've been looking for you. |
| *to* | Kaninda | It's here counts, just. |

- Act Two, Scene 11 (pages 71–2)
- Act Two, Scene 15 (pages 84–6)

from   THEO   Lick-spittled!?
to   THEO   I survive my way, you survive yours.

2   Copy and complete the character-gram for Laura below.

Laura Rose: 'too good to go to heaven'?

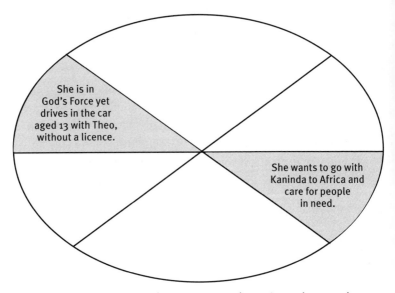

She is in God's Force yet drives in the car aged 13 with Theo, without a licence.

She wants to go with Kaninda to Africa and care for people in need.

Decide whether your character-gram shows Laura in a good or bad light.

3   **As a class,** hold a formal discussion or debate about Laura and how she comes over in the play. One view of her could be that she is truly 'God's soldier', as her parents like to call her. An opposite view could be that she is only 'a good person' when she gets herself into trouble and needs get her 'credit back with God' (page 86).

What have I learnt?

- How has this activity taught you the best way to make notes quickly and accurately?
- What have you learnt about how the playwright presents a major character?
- How did this activity help you to argue your case in a class debate/discussion?

Activity 5: Planning a performance

Learning outcomes

You will:

- explore the use of staging, setting and scenery
- describe and explain accurately.

You will do this by imagining you are the producer of the play. You will plan a performance of *Little Soldier* for students in your year group who have not read it.

1   Remind yourselves of what Bernard Ashley writes on pages iv–v about staging this play. Then read aloud the following four scenes.

- The pre-scene (page 3).
- Act One, Scenes 5 and 6 (pages 8–13), where we first meet the two gangs.
- Act One, Scenes 12 and 14 (pages 18–19 and 26–30), where the action includes 'flashbacks' to Africa.
- Act Two, Scenes 17 to 20 (pages 35–42), which make up the ending of the play.

2   As a class, discuss these questions.

   a   Why is *Little Soldier* different from many other plays in its use of settings, scenery and changes from scene to scene?

   b   In a performance, how could you make use of back projections, slides, signs, 'flown-in' scenery and props?

   c   What 'style' of production would best suit your audience?

- A simple 'studio'/'open space' set, or a traditional platform stage set?
- A cast of 50, or fewer actors playing several parts each?

- Some sections to be done in mime or tableau (e.g. the big gang fight in the Mall), or use to be made of every word of the dialogue as written?
- Full, realistic costume for all the characters, or just a few items to mark them out?

3   Draw on your class discussion to write production notes for any **two** or **three** of the scenes listed in **1** (on page 108). Your production notes should *describe* how the scenes will be presented on stage and *explain* your reasons for presenting them in a particular way.

What have I learnt?

- What have you learnt about the terminology used to describe the staging of a play?
- How do scenery, setting and props help bring a play to life?
- How has this activity taught you what a producer's job involves? (Does this job appeal to you?)

Activity 6: The title of the play

Learning outcomes

You will:

- explore specific characters
- use evidence from the play
- organise and present your ideas
- write for a specific purpose.

You will do this by considering how the play's title, *Little Soldier*, applies to the characters and themes within it.

1   Brainstorm your ideas about which character or characters *Little Soldier* is used to describe. You should put the spotlight on each of the following characters.

   a   Kaninda
   b   Laura
   c   Faustin
   d   Queen Max (or Baz)

   Make a chart like the one below to show what you decide. Use bullet points.

Who does the play's title apply to?			
CHARACTER A Kaninda *because*	**CHARACTER B** Laura *because*	**CHARACTER C** Faustin *because*	**CHARACTER D** Queen Max (or Baz) *because*
•	•	•	•

   Aim to make three entries in each column. Make sure your **because** points are clearly thought-out.

2   Use the chart to decide who you think Bernard Ashley feels is the *Little Soldier*, and why. If you decide that the title can apply to several characters, talk about how they are *different* kinds of 'soldier'. Make brief notes on your decisions.

3   By yourself, write the following literature essay.

Explain why you think Bernard Ashley chose *Little Soldier* as the title of his play. How does it draw our attention to the play's themes and ideas, as well as its characters?

Use evidence and quotations from the text to back up the points you make.

What have I learnt?

- What have you learnt about how writers choose the titles of their plays, novels and studies with great care?
- What have you learnt about how the playwright uses different characters to convey the themes/ideas in his play?
- How has this activity taught you how useful it is to make diagrammatic notes when planning a literature essay?

Activity 7: A different outcome

Learning outcomes

You will:

- select and analyse a scene
- narrow down and organise your ideas
- write for a specific purpose
- perform to an audience.

You will do this by choosing a scene from the play and imagining that it has a different outcome. Then you will write your own version of your chosen scene and perform it.

1   Which scenes from the play do you think could have a different outcome from the one provided by the playwright? Decide on a short list, which might include:

- Act One, Scene 14, in which Kaninda is at school in London, then in Lasai
- Act Two, Scene 2, in which Kaninda does his 'run' and Laura saves him from falling into the river
- Act Two, Scene 12, in which Dolly comes out of her coma
- Act Two, Scene 17, in which Faustin and Kaninda talk about the tribal war in Lasai and make peace with one another.

There are many other scenes you could choose.

2   Choose which scene you are going to work on. Then discuss:

- how you will change the events
- whether you will keep exactly the same characters or introduce some new ones
- how you will make your version both clear to understand and dramatic.

3   Write your version of the scene. Think about the following three things:

- the dialogue – you need to make this realistic

- the stage directions – write these in the same style Bernard Ashley uses
- the need to build your scene to a climax that will 'work' on stage and grip the audience.

4   Perform your scene. Afterwards, think about how effective each scene was, and why.

What have I learnt?

- What skills have you used/developed in this activity?
- What has this activity taught you about what it feels like to write part of a play?
- What have you learnt about how scripting a drama is a different kind of challenge from writing a story?
- How did it feel to perform in front of others? Did you enjoy it and were you good at it?

Activity 8: Laura

Learning outcomes

You will:

- investigate the script, selecting relevant information
- write for a specific purpose, for a specific audience.

You will do this by imagining that Laura recovers from her injuries. Then put yourself in her place and reflect, in writing, on some of her experiences.

1   Scan the play to recall details about the following events/ situations involving Laura:

- her relationship with Theo
- the car accident
- her visit to the hospital to see Dolly
- her relationship with Kaninda, including her plan to go to Africa with him
- the gang fight at the Millennium Mall.

Talk about how she will feel about these events/situations now. Remember, she has almost died. She may see some things she did, and some of the situations she got involved with, in a different light.

2   Plan a private letter from Laura, who is still in hospital, to her parents. In the letter, she confides the full truth about the things she did during the time covered by the play, and expresses her honest feelings about these. She also tells her parents what she has learned from her experiences and what she plans to do with her future. When you have finished planning, write Laura's letter. Remember, she is an intelligent 13 year-old who feels deeply about things. She would write in a direct, sincere way and in a straightforward style.

What have I learnt about?

- How has this activity taught you about seeing the events of the play from one character's viewpoint? How is this different from seeing the events as a reader or spectator?
- What have you learnt about the importance of being able to show empathy with a character in order to understand them fully?
- What have you learnt about the difference between writing 'in role' and writing your own 'account' or 'essay' on a text?

GLOSSARY

Abraham Lincoln the American president who first abolished slavery under the Emancipation Proclamation
atrocity act of violence
avanti Italian for 'go'

Babylon black slang for police
blow rubbish or nonesense

cabbies cab or taxi drivers
Chevvy, Cadillac, Eldorado classic American car
can o' squirt can of graffiti paint
ciao Italian for 'goodbye'
Citadel in the Salvation Army (or the play's 'God's Force') a building where meetings are held
court martial military court

doin' time prison sentence
doz stupid person

Five Ks Sikh male symbols, worn sometimes in token form: Kesh – uncut hair, Kangha – comb used to keep hair clean, Kara – metal bangle, Kaccha – knee-length underwear, Kirpan – small dagger
foliage gobo a gobo is a stage light that projects a 'shadow' in a particular shape to help a scene's setting; e.g. of foliage, windows, clouds

graffiti tag signature sprayed on a wall by a graffiti artist

Indianapolis Five Hundred car race in Indianapolis, USA
initiation test for getting into a gang
inside prison

KM17 an automatic weapon

lick-spittled cleaned using spit

lim limousine – upmarket car

lock-up car garage found in housing estates

lumped 'lumped-up' or 'feeling lumpy' is to feel upset

mondo fighter amazing fighter

mullah defeat!

Old Bill police

old Cayoo Theo's invented exciting destination

'port' position a military way of carrying a rifle diagonally across the body with the barrel close to the left shoulder

posho popular East African dish, 'top posho' containing more meat

poxy sub-standard

ringin' it criminal slang for fixing false number plates to a car

rip-off an unlawful scheme, also an unfair deal

saffron robes robes of a saffron colour worn by Buddhist monks

salwar kameez tunic and trousers worn by Punjabi females

scappare Italian for escape

scoot rush, hurry

scrags to pull roughly

skull cap worn by Jewish males

slate account held at a shop

small it make yourself scarce

sussed suspected (not necessarily caught as a result of being 'sussed')

suthink something

Tante aunt

Thorpe Park skin peeler scary ride at Thorpe Park theme park

vincitore Italian for 'winner'

yellow cowardly